THE UNIVERSITY OF CHICAGO

DIFFUSION OF THE DECISION TO IRRIGATE

SIMULATION OF THE SPREAD OF A NEW RESOURCE MANAGEMENT PRACTICE IN THE COLORADO NORTHERN HIGH PLAINS

DEPARTMENT OF GEOGRAPHY

RESEARCH PAPER NO. 97

By

LEONARD W. BOWDEN

CHICAGO · ILLINOIS

1965

Library of Congress Catalog Card Number: 65-22712

Research grants from the University of California, Riverside and the University of Southern California supported this study in part. Funds supplied by the Dry-Lands Institute, University of California, Riverside, permitted the updating of information for Chapter V.

ACKNOWLEDGMENTS

This monograph encompasses five years of observing the impact of pump irrigation in the Colorado Northern High Plains. The cooperation and guidance of many persons were involved in its completion.

Professor Tim K. Kelley of the University of Colorado encouraged me to begin the study of western Yuma County in an attempt to interpret the problems irrigation might present or solve in a semi-arid region. Professor Robert W. Kates of Clark University directed, criticized, and contributed many positive suggestions which led to this publication. To these teachers I owe much for their inspiration and understanding.

Practical field research was accomplished only with the active participation of farmers, ranchers, civil officials, and others in the study area, and various research centers--such as the Ground Water Division of USGS, Denver, and the Colorado State Engineers Office. Vital information was gleaned from well drillers, county agents, bankers, merchants, irrigators, and non-irrigators. For example, men like Harold Bennett of the Federal Land Bank furnished well logs, or Jim Vincent who operates a super market and pharmacy but takes time to participate in a multi-county planning board to help resolve ground water problems of the area--these contributed realism to this research.

Riverside, California
April, 1965

TO CHESTER BOWDEN AND HOMER MURPHY
pioneers, homesteaders, farmers of the High Plains — my grandfathers

MANUSCRIPT TYPED BY PEGGY HUFFMAN

MAPS DRAFTED BY ROY ELLEDGE

COVER DESIGNED BY MARY ANN GRIFFIN

TABLE OF CONTENTS

vii

LIST OF ILLUSTRATIONS

xi

LIST OF TABLES

THE FUTURE OF PUMP IRRIGATION
IN THE COLORADO NORTHERN HIGH PLAINS

Introduction of pump irrigation to the Colorado Northern
High Plains, a region of dryland farming and cattle grazing, involves a decision to develop and use a non-renewable water resource.
This change in resource practice affects local and regional conditions that previously adhered to the winter wheat and cattle raising economy. The region has incurred considerable change in past
resource use but has stabilized in many respects since the end of
the dust bowl and depression. Improvements in summer fallow
methods, increased dependence on stubble mulching and soil packing
by modern farm implements make the area a productive site for dryland farming and grazing when moisture is available. Therefore,
scientific farming techniques enable the local farmer to effec-
tively utilize the agriculturally marginal precipitation that
averages 17 inches per year.

Despite the overt prosperity of the last two decades, the
High Plains farmers experienced an economic squeeze during the
1950's--as did most other wheat producers. To compensate for
government grain acreage restrictions, sagging farm income, land
idled by farm programs, unfavorable weather conditions, etc.,
residents enlarged their cattle feeding facilities. Unfortunately,

short but severe droughts left the cattle feeder with large herds and no feed crops or pasture. Some farmers began installing pump irrigation in an attempt to counteract this situation.

Before 1960, the occurrence of ground water in the area was of regional importance only as a source of domestic and stock well supply. Except for a few pioneer irrigators, ground water as a supplier of potential irrigation water received scant attention. Few scientific investigations had been made and quality or quantity of ground water was at best an educated guess. The innovation of irrigation, therefore, offers numerous unsolved problems and creates certain basic questions: Is pump irrigation physically possible? Economically gainful? Socially acceptable? Legally permissible? What is the role that irrigation can or will play in the future environment of this semi-arid plains region?

Investigation shows that in the unconsolidated Ogallala aquifer, which underlies the Colorado Northern High Plains, wells pumping from more than 50 feet of saturated sand and gravel will generally supply a minimum of 500 gallons per minute. This amount is the minimum requirement at this latitude for 120 acres of hybrid corn, the dominant irrigated crop. From the well log data of numerous stock and domestic wells, the zone of irrigation potential may be delimited by overlaying a choropleth of the ground water supply with a land classification map, using Class I and Class II as potentially irrigable.

Having identified a potential irrigation area, the growth of pump irrigation and the influence of past and present well lo-cations on future installations may be studied. In January, 1963,

there were 435 producing irrigation wells in the 10,000 square
mile area. About 1 per cent of the arable land was being irrigated.
Thus, irrigation is just beginning in the Colorado High Plains.
More irrigation is physically possible.

It is important to ascertain why the decision to begin
pump irrigation occurs. Surveys and interviews point out the
following factors as inducements to irrigation: (1) restricted
dryland acreage from government controls which left idle land;
(2) fear of drought; (3) new machinery to supply and carry irrigation water; (4) stable beef prices that promoted demands for feed
lots which require feed crops; (5) new sources of credit or investment in well financing; (6) available cheap power to operate pump
units; and, recently (7) easing of government restriction on domestic sugar beet production.[1]

Pump irrigation entails an expensive capital outlay--as
much as $40,000 for well and land. In addition to high cost,
other inhibiting factors exist: (1) a lack of young people to
perform the hard work of irrigated farming; (2) larger farm sites
under the control of a single, middle aged individual who is not
interested in making an expensive, unproven change; (3) sagging
farm produce prices; (4) little education regarding methods of
irrigation; (5) high costs of new farming equipment; and (6)

---

[1] A drop in beef prices in 1963 may temporarily affect the
growth in pump irrigation for the production of feeder crops.
However, because irrigation is planned with long-term goals, the
influence of short-term price decreases should have little impact.
The decline in number of well installations for feed crops is
probably offset by the chance to experiment with sugar beets.

uncertainty about the ground water supply. There is not one or even a combination of reasons that clearly explains why the spatial pattern of irrigation development exists as it does at present. Each innovator has specific motives for adopting irrigation or rejecting it. But, from a regional perspective, the pattern for irrigation development appears to spread through time from a central nucleus in a patterned, but randomly varying way.

There is in this apparent spread an identifiable grouping of newer wells around the earlier (core) installations. The probability of a new well occurrence decreases with increasing distance from the core. Possibly, new wells were considered because of the communication of the idea through face-to-face contacts which depend upon propinquity, along with other positive motivating factors. If an established well motivated a neighbor to install, then there should be a receiver-teller network of communication within this region. Once such a network is identified, a "mean information field" (MIF) of the probability of ideas spreading at a measurable rate from existing locations can be established. A method for explaining the present location and projecting future development of pump irrigation can then be postulated from this "mean information field," which is the probability distribution of contacts over space. Simulating the diffusion of wells through space and time, using probability distribution, is one aspect of this study.

To discover the communication network and MIF a modification of Hägerstrand's Monte Carlo simulation of diffusion method may be used. The pattern of communication was developed in this study from two sources--the number of long distance telephone calls between towns within the region relative to their distance apart, and the number of people who attended a free barbecue, relative to the distance traveled to the barbecue location. With this information the probability of communication per unit of distance can be obtained by least squares procedures. Using probability of occurrence per unit distance, and assuming no directional bias, such data can be plotted on an azimuthal grid to show the spatial distribution of the probability of contact per unit distance.

The grid is applied as follows: (1) using a map of operating well locations, the center of the grid is placed on a well, and a selection made from a table of random numbers. Locating that number on the grid gives the location of a receiver of the idea from the teller well. (2) Each established well tells a new well the following year, but if the receiver is outside the delimited potential irrigation area the telling is disregarded and the grid moved to another well and a new random number chosen. (3) If the random location occurs within a mile of a teller well or another well, the grid is moved on. (4) The simulation is continued until the saturation point of 16 wells per township is reached.

Utilizing this method, ten simulation runs were performed in this study using 1948 well locations as an initial distribution. Simulated totals for 1962 fell within 10 per cent of the actual total and the spatial distribution conformed to the real pattern.

With the 1962 known locations as starting points the same simulation procedure was performed through 1975 and 1990.[1]

The simulated results provide estimates of the ground water that irrigation will demand. The Ogallala aquifer contains some 30 million acre feet of permanently stored water recoverable for potential irrigation; the simulation model shows that irrigation should produce accumulative withdrawal of about 20 million acre feet by 1990.[2]

The validity of these findings, based on simulation, can be best tested by time in the Colorado High Plains and in comparable regions. Of prime purpose here is to project future ground water use, a vital component in a change to pump irrigation for this area and suggest occurrences that the water user must anticipate if proper management is to be achieved.

Projections of the Future Scene

A framework of possible, gainful, acceptable, and permissible conditions may be used to interpret reasons for change in resource practices and for identifying transition stages. Using these same criteria the future situation for pump irrigation in the study area may be evaluated.

---

[1] The number of wells to be located per year can also be taken from a table of two-digit random numbers whose maximum values were below the limits of a trend curve of yearly well installation that reached its maximum in 1970.

[2] In addition to a 1 inch annual recharge by precipitation.

Relative to Physical Possibility

Basic to the future of pump irrigation in the Colorado High Plains is the quantity of available ground water. Assuming that the physical area delimited in Chapter II and the model projection from Chapter IV are valid, there is little danger of immediate water depletion. There should be no more than 2,000 wells by the 21st Century, and the physical possibility of ground water existing for irrigation will continue. However, the ground water supply can be enhanced and protected by practices that will not impede development of pump irrigation. For example, if wells are spaced two to three miles apart to prevent lowering of the water table by coalescence of "cones of depression," more practical and long term results can be anticipated. This will require considerable cooperation among resource managers or probably government control.

If present farm size is doubled by 1990, there could then be one well per farm unit. Irrigated acreage, supported by approximately 1,800 to 2,000 wells, will be formed on each farm as part of a larger, more complex operation. The landscape picture at that time should reveal installations that are widely spaced, assuming that the area remains devoted to similar crops and cattle feeding as now exist and irrigation is complemental[1] to a large, integrated agricultural enterprise.

---

[1] It would be improper to modify the irrigation now being performed by terms such as supplemental, integrated, or converted; therefore, "complemental" irrigation is considered most appropriate for the time being.

Demand for intensive and widespread irrigation could materialize and cause ground water depletion. Should urbanization invade the Colorado Piedmont and Platte and Arkansas basins taking them out of agricultural production, sugar beets, dairy, or "truck" type crop requirements for the increased population could intensify land use in the High Plains. Also, urban demands for water might reallocate the amount available for surface irrigation in the adjacent rivers, throwing the demands for water to produce crops into the High Plains. Events like these could very well place pressure on the Ogallala water supply and the position of irrigation in the High Plains. Thus far, however, these occurrences seem unlikely for several decades; and if technological improvements in agriculture continue to meet the food demands of an urban nation, there should be no unforeseen or outside demands on Colorado High Plains water.

Relative to Legal Permissibility

Legal controls of ground water use in the Colorado Northern High Plains can be enforced should there be a serious depletion problem in the next several decades. Use of a non-renewable resource often implies a need for conservation. Until recently, water rights and regulations in Colorado have been concerned only with established surface irrigation in the Piedmont, San Luis Valley, and Western Slope developments.

After much delay, the state of Colorado Ground Water Law was initiated May 1, 1957, providing a Ground Water Commission of eight to supervise the enforcement of the Act. This law requires a statement of use for all existing wells and registration of all present and planned wells, with the exception of stock and domestic wells with limited discharge. Permits are necessary to drill new wells and the Commission, in cooperation with the state engineer, has power to regulate driller licensing and drilling provisions. The Commission has authority to close all areas designated critical or misused. But the technical aspects of ground water advising are the responsibility of the engineer. This law, if applied, can prevent over pumping of a ground water aquifer if depletion is threatened. Unfortunately, the Ogallala is not readily rechargeable and its water is non-recoverable once applied to the land. By the time the Commission could act, the Ogallala would be mined beyond salvage because the law clearly states that evidence of depletion must be presented. Therefore, even with a well defined water law, use and misuse of Ogallala water will remain in the hands of the individual well and land owners.[1]

The water tenure issue will come to the front in local situations long before any mining or action by the Ground Water

---

[1] Another possible legal inequality is that the State of Colorado is divided into Water Control Districts. The Ogallala, which is a physical part of the greater Kansas River Basin, is considered by the State Water Commission as being divided between the South Platte Water District and the Arkansas River Water District. Therefore, it could be subjected to rules and regulations developed for surface water irrigation of these two river basins. Fortunately, the Water Commission has proposed a redistricting that will make the Colorado High Plains a separate control district and local planning groups are being formed to suggest legislative action needed to control or reorganize the present situation.

Commission. Because ground water is a sub-surface resource, the law finds its definition and control difficult. Questions, however, that legislation will have to answer sooner or later are: Does sinking a well before a neighbor drills one give a farmer prior appropriation rights to the ground water that flows from under the neighbor's land? If a well lowers the water table, who is responsible for replenishment or compensating for the loss to adjacent land? Is ground water a mineral resource that can be used, sold, or retained? Several cattlemen are already concerned that shallow stock wells adjacent to irrigation wells may go dry unless redrilled.

Taxes also have legal implications, and they will increase as local adjustors begin to realize the greater value per unit of irrigated land in contrast to dryland acreages. At present each county assesses its own wells and establishes taxation rules. All but one county tax on irrigated acreage rather than on water used. But to tax an irrigator by water used rather than acres covered will hopefully become widespread in the next decade as assessors realize the importance of this method as a realistic step toward proper water management.

Relative to Social Acceptability and Economic Gainfulness

Present social and economic trends[1] will gain momentum with or without the integration of pump irrigation. A return to the family farm and an increasing local consumer population are

---

[1]Declining population, lower profits per unit of land, fewer but older farmers, and so on.

highly doubtful. Average farm size has doubled in the past 30 years, and there is no evidence of a slowing of this trend. Farm units are now or soon will be managed and operated more automatically than manually. These future corporate enterprises will have to be controlled and supervised by educated managers. Therefore, potential young farmers without large investment capital will have little opportunity to enter agriculture except as members of this select labor force, hired to oversee the enterprise. Centralized market towns will disappear or be fewer and serve as housing and support units for the small "sidewalk" populace.

Irrigation will supplement the larger dryland operation, and land use by crop type should remain proportionally the same. The main difference will be in the utilization of machines to a greater degree and the adoption of a scientific crop and animal management methods. Thus a mosaic of grain, irrigated crops, and cattle raising will be present, each complementing and subsidizing one another during periods of individual declines in marketability. This might be compared to the agricultural interdependence for self-sufficiency in the 1920's, when the general farm attempted to integrate activities. The principal difference in the future will be the few persons involved on each farm, the tremendous increase in scale of operation, and the absence of self-sufficiency in terms of the standard of living of the farm populace.

Agricultural income per farm unit will be great, but income per acre will be less than today. The large acreages will require credit and investment on a scale that will demand close

supervision, as profit margins will be narrow, even though the
overall return may be equal to that of many businesses. Farm
laborers, few but skilled, will probably be unionized.

In general, farming will be more scientific, automated,
and tightly controlled on the corporate acreages. Tillage and
harvest will take much less time than today as technology improves.
Perhaps the only time consuming process will be growth and maturation of plants and animals. These too may be accelerated by advances in seed grains, fertilizers, husbandry, and so forth.

Irrigation: A Permanent Fixture on the Landscape

Change in American agriculture is reflected throughout
the Colorado Northern High Plains. Advances in production machinery and techniques that occurred during the first half of the
twentieth century are but indicators of the remarkable farming
improvements yet to come. There is little doubt that pump irrigation will play a significant role in the changing agricultural
environment of the region. Pump wells have evolved beyond the
experimental stage and offer farmers a tool that helps him escape
the whims of an unpredictable climate and adjust to fluctuating
economic conditions.

Irrigation is not a panacea for the complex farm problems
of today or tomorrow for the High Plains, but it can aid in over-
coming many of them as a supplement to the agricultural scene.
Therefore, pump irrigation can and should be permanent for the
twentieth century, at least. The greatest potential in utilizing

the ground water supply of the Ogallala aquifer may be to help
establish a feeder crop supply for a meat producing region that can
fulfill the demands of a gigantic and prosperous urban American
society. Irrigation also offers a buffer for the farmer who is
financially trapped by the fluctuating market demands of single
crop wheat production.

Mis-use and mis-management can threaten the regional
ground water supply eventually, but if a trend toward larger,
better managed, intelligently supervised farm units is maintained,
the trained personnel who operate corporate farm enterprises will
have to be made aware of the advantages of long term efficient
resource management. This thesis is presented to aid the resource
manager of the Colorado Northern High Plains in achieving this
awareness.

CHAPTER I

HISTORICAL USE OF HIGH PLAINS RESOURCES

Agricultural resource development in the Colorado Northern High Plains involves periods of failure and despair alternating with years of success and prosperity. Within this steppe
region, where climatic conditions vary yearly from humid to arid,
making a living above a subsistence level in agriculture is an
extraordinary challenge. Today's main economic base, initiated
about 1885, is dryland farming.[1] It has survived a variety of
trials while passing through stages of changing resource use. The
present environment is undergoing change as adjustments in the
utilization of the resource base take place due to the increasing
economic requirements for agricultural survival in a primarily
urban nation. Examination of the events that have shaped past
resource practice is essential to understanding ways in which this
environmental change are shaping agriculture and resource use

---

[1]Dryland farming is different from dry farming. Dryland
farming refers to crops grown through techniques to conserve or
salvage limited amounts of water. One method is the "summer-
fallow" technique in which the fields are allowed to lie idle for
one growing season to collect soil moisture to be used the following year. The fields are cultivated to retard weeds which tran-
spire moisture. Dry farming means simply "without irrigation."

today. By the same token, understanding of these events is
critical for projecting future use of resources in the Colorado
Northern High Plains. One such projection, that of the diffusion
of pump irrigation in the region, is the central concern of this
study, and procedures are developed to simulate this diffusion process.

Definition of "Resource Practices"

A description of patterns or practices of agricultural
resource use should be general but applicable and accurate when
applied to a local situation. Walter Firey proposes a scheme which
classifies resources practices as:

Possible	or	Not Possible
Adoptable	or	Not Adoptable
Gainful	or	Not Gainful[1]

Firey visualizes a usable or dynamic resource complex as employing
a "set of practices" taken from all the possible, adoptable, gainful practices and that their intersection designates resource use.

> An event which recurs in time and which involves
> somewhat the same combination of human and bio-
> physical factors may be called a resource process.
> Thus plowing with oxen constitutes one process;
> plowing with horses constitutes another process.
> To the economist a process may be identified
> with a particular proportioning of some desig-
> nated productive factors. To the ecologist
> or geographer, a process may be identified with
> a particular association of organic and physical
> elements in a given habitat. ...we may adopt
> the term resource system as a generic designation
> of any set of resource processes, irrespective
> of the structural character which that set may
> or may not have . . . a particular resource

---

[1]Walter Firey, Man, Mind, and Land, (Glencoe, Illinois:
The Free Press), 1960, pp. 36-37.

> system might be viewed as consisting of the tools
> which are customarily employed; the combinations
> and sequences in which they are used; the animals
> employed; . . . the crops grown . . . the soils
> cultivated . . . productive organization of the
> population . . . relevant conceptual categories
> . . . and . . . particular nexus of organic and
> physical processes . . . (There are) two varieties
> of resource systems . . . within a set of resource
> processes. Both are taken as limiting cases. One
> of them, which we propose to call a resource com-
> plex, shows some constancy and stability in the
> face of changes that are external to itself. The
> other, . . . resource congeries, shows no such
> stability but varies widely in response to ex-
> ternal changes. The former type of system has a
> certain lawfulness which expresses the invariance
> properties that it possesses as a structural
> whole; its component processes may be given a
> special designation: resources practices.[1]

During the last 80 years, the Colorado High Plains has shown a

stable and consistent resource complex involving agriculture.

The methods used to maintain this complex, i. e., resources prac-

tices, have varied enough so that particular practices at particu-

lar times can be categorized into stages of development.

The breadth of Firey's concept permits application easily

to a particular region. Working within his framework a modifica-

tion enhances the validity, lucidity, and understanding of changes

which have occurred in the High Plains. Instead of three classi-

fications, the "sets of practices" are increased to four: possible,

gainful, acceptable, and permissible. To achieve clarity, the

practices are either:

Physically Possible or Not Physically Possible

Economically Gainful or Not Economically Gainful

---

[1]Ibid., pp. 13-15.

Socially Acceptable or Not Socially Acceptable

Legally Permissible or Not Legally Permissible

Developed or potential resource use is designated as the area
where the four practices form an identifiable or projectable part
of the landscape.

The assumption is that any stage of past resource development contained practices that fell within all four categories;
conversely, an impedence to past resource use or development can
be attributed to the absence of one or more of the four essentials.
Sequences of resource use which involved a break up of the set are
believed to have changed resource practice. Illustrations of how
the four classifications of practices might affect decisions are
as follows:

Physically Possible--It is physically possible to produce almost
all mid-latitude grains and grasses as well as most livestock in the
High Plains environment. However, it is presently impossible to
grow cotton because of the short, 145-day growing season in the
area or to establish citrus orchards due to frosts and freezes.
The farmer (or resource manager) then has a narrow range of decision controls in which to find a productive outlet. Although scientific management and new techniques continually expand the con-
fines of the physical environment, the manager must measure possible and marginally possible practices against how much he will pay
to modify or create a new or artifical environment.

Economically Gainful--Any resource use which produces a livelihood
or a profit is economically gainful. Often, "economically gainful"
means the resource use which is most gainful. A farmer in the

Colorado High Plains may earn a profit on wheat, safflower, or potatoes, or he may raise turkeys or complement dryland wheat with irrigated feed crops and cattle. Although all are possible, he will likely choose the one or a combination of activities which makes the most profit. However, if he abandons agriculture and builds a golf course or game refuge, he changes the resource process as well as the resource practice. But, then he is confronted with opinions and pressures by his society. In the modern farming era where independence and self sufficiency diminishes yearly, acceptability is critical.

Socially Acceptable--Acceptability may involve conditions which influence resource use because of peoples' cultural or social attitudes. Until recently, it was of considerable pride to plow the straightest furrow, or breed the "fattest" herd bull, regardless of the dangers of soil erosion or inferior stock replacement. A significant example of cultural inacceptability occurred when a proposed commercial feed lot--intended to market local surplus feed crops--was not established because townspeople found the presence of a "smelly" feeder lot objectionable and pressured authorities to prevent it. This incident indicates how individuals or groups will combine law and society to inhibit practices even when the practice is possible or gainful.

Legally Permissible--Legality includes controls of resource use, such as control of agricultural production through restricted acreage or subsidies and may be identified at local, state, or federal government levels. Permissibility encourages or restricts resource development. Government control can encourage development of one resource by curtailing acreage devoted to another as when a wheat farmer uses land idled by restrictions to produce feed crops or reseed to grass. Water laws, public land policy, tax structure, and land zoning are all considered legal influences. Decision making, at the individual level, is then greatly dependent upon decisions of group or government levels. This influence makes everyone involved a resource manager, with each level contributing a decision on how to use (or circumvent) a higher decision.

The disruption of a stable relationship among the resource practices often occurs as a result of a series of complex, related events. For example, production of sugar beets in the Colorado Northern High Plains is, as yet, insignificant, but in the adjoining South Platte Valley of the Colorado Piedmont, sugar beets are the major part of the resource complex. Legal control of irrigation water and acreage control under government subsidy programs restrict allotment of water or beet acreage outside the South Platte Valley. These two restrictions are an anachronism as the surface water of the Platte is overcommitted due to existing rights and cannot supply sufficient water to satisfy internal demands for allotted acreages.[1] Assignment of part of the beet acreage to the High Plains could encourage development of a pump irrigated, sugar beet producing economy. But this assignment is dependent upon decisions made at federal levels, which depend on international

---

[1] At the same time this water is yearned for by the expanding urban population of Denver.

situations, etc. It is physically possible, probably economically gainful, and socially acceptable[1] to grow sugar beets in the High Plains, but it is _not_ legally permissible for every irrigator to produce and market beets even if he decides to do so.

Stages of Resource Development
in the Colorado Northern High Plains

In the Northern High Plains of Colorado (Figure 1), the sequence of past resource development falls into five identifiable periods, characterized by: open range grazing; general farming; dust, depression, and crop failure; one crop economy; and dryland farming and cattle feeding. One more category, pump irrigation, is now becoming a part of the landscape and its introduction, diffusion, and effects are the actual concern in this study of the region.

Early Settlement and the Disappearance of Range Land

In the late nineteenth century westward expansion brought cattlemen and farmers to the Colorado High Plains, which were once considered uninhabitable.[2] After the Civil War, the area was mostly open range. But as the railroads pushed west to Denver in the 1880's, they brought an influx of homesteaders. Cattlemen welcomed the railroad as a bolster to the marketing of livestock;

---

[1]The social acceptability of sugar beet production is new to the local populace of the High Plains. These people have long had a distaste for the "stoop" and migratory labor necessary to cultivate and harvest the crop. Now, however, advancements in mechanized sugar beet production have eliminated this "disadvantage."

[2]Early geographers and explorers referred to this area as the Great American Desert.

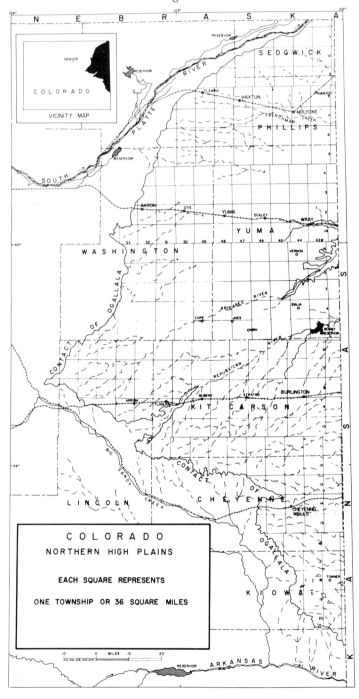

Figure 1.   The western boundary is delimited by the Ogallala
geologic formation.

but they did not appreciate how soon it would hasten the end of open range grazing as it brought in the agrarian homesteaders.[1] Other conditions contributed to the settlement of the High Plains. The Homestead Act of 1862, offered 160 acres of public domain to any person who was the head of a family and an American citizen, after five years occupancy and improvements on the land. Also, a new agricultural generation was evolving which did not depend on forests and water supplies because of the use of sod houses, barbed wire, drilled wells, windmills, and the steel plow.[2]

After breaking the sod on his claim, the early settler had to find a domestic and stock water supply. It was vital to begin a time-consuming and expensive search for ground water as soon as a well driller could be hired and windmill equipment purchased. The landscape soon became dotted with windmill towers.

Unfortunately, settlers from the humid East were unaware of the variable characteristics of this western climate (Figure 2). Drought struck in 1890, and in the spring of 1892, the continuing dry weather was accompanied by hordes of locusts who devoured crops. The insects appeared as black clouds that ate everything from house

---

[1]Ralph H. Brown, <u>Historical Geography of the United States</u>, (New York: Harcourt, Brace and Co., 1951). This geographer lists overspeculation by ambitious cattle companies, unstable meat prices in the East, a series of disastrous winters that froze thousands of cattle, over crowding of ranges, and lack of legislative control, combined with the advance of the agricultural frontier, as other factors which hastened the end of open range cattle grazing.

[2]C. Warren Thornthwaite, "Climate and Settlement in the Great Plains," <u>Climate and Man, Yearbook of Agriculture</u>, 1941, (Washington, D. C.: U. S. Government Printing Office, 1941), p. 184.

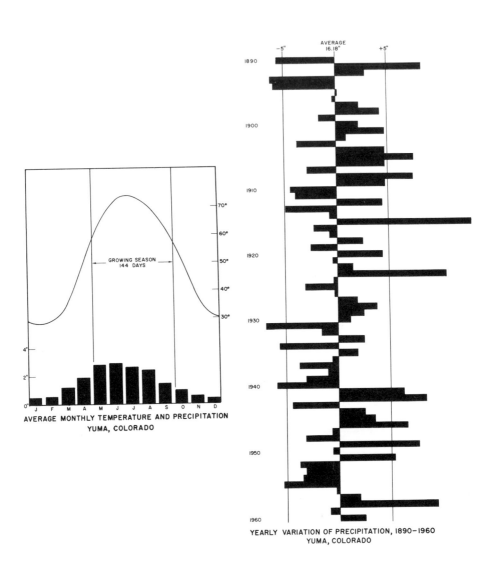

GROWING SEASON
144 DAYS

AVERAGE MONTHLY TEMPERATURE AND PRECIPITATION
YUMA, COLORADO

AVERAGE
16.18"

YEARLY VARIATION OF PRECIPITATION, 1890–1960
YUMA, COLORADO

Figure 2

curtains to the horses' leather harnesses. Even in 1896, a year of 16 inches of rainfall, grasshoppers destroyed every crop.[1] Eventually much of the High Plains was returned to range because adverse economic and climatic conditions meant bankruptcy to homesteaders.

Only the factor of social acceptability applied throughout the homesteading period. Acceptability of an agrarian way of life could not sustain economic development, however. The homesteader emulated the way of life he had known previously and was considered a stable and acceptable part of the cultural environment.[2] But limitations to resource development such as drought alternating with torrential rains, pounding hail, and devastating blizzards were prohibitive. The single positive physical factor at that time was the general availability of fertile, brown, chestnut, and chernozem soils that had developed under the short prairie grasses. But to plow one quarter section of land (which was not enough land to support a family during a low rainfall year) with oxen or horses took as long as three years.

General Farming and the Family Size Farm

In 1896, the drought broke in the Colorado High Plains, and by 1900 railroads and real estate promotion built another land boom. Sufficient precipitation continued for several years and encouraged new settlement. Low income during the national depression in 1893 meant economic loss, but there was also

---

[1] John Abbot, "Looking Backward," Yuma Pioneer, July 6 and July 19, 1951.

[2] Despite tales of "rancher-nester" conflicts that were popular but untrue.

encouragement in legal permissibility when in 1903, Congress increased the homesteader's claim from 160 to 320 acres.[1] After legality became less restrictive because of the amendment to the Homestead Act, farm implement manufacturers promoted sales of a new soil packing plow that maintained a "dust mulch" on the surface of the land. The dust mulch technique created finely textured, supposedly more fertile, soil with moisture retention. Government experiment farms warned that if rainfall diminished the powdery mulch could mean severe land erosion. But few farmers and ranchers were concerned about a brief dry spell in 1910-1913 as the following years brought rain and a world war. The use of dust mulch appeared highly advantageous; small grain demand was high and every available acre was plowed and planted. Wheat sold for $2.70 a bushel.[2] Thus the resource use involving the production of wheat and other small grain was possible, acceptable, gainful and permissible.

Although farm power was furnished by draft horses[3] for the most part, mechanization was making an impact by the 1920's. On a typical farm, the improved machinery cultivated spring wheat and rye. The following year a field was planted in corn or sorghum and cultivated by horse power; after that the field would be

[1] Alvin T. Steinel, History of Agriculture in Colorado, (Ft. Collins, Colorado: The State Agricultural College), 1916, pp. 131-134.

[2] Vance Johnson, Heaven's Tableland, (New York: Farrar, Strauss and Co.), 1947, pp. 47-48.

[3] Consequently an estimated fourth of the farm acreage was devoted to feed crops for the draft animals.

replanted in another grain such as barley, oats, or back to wheat.

Farms were practically self-sufficient.[1] Families were large and hired men completed the work force. If the farm operator lived on Class I land[2] with high fertility and moisture retention, a profitable enterprise was possible on 640 acres (one section). In addition, a dozen cows, two dozen hogs, and 200 chickens might supplement the land income. Should one crop fail, another could compensate for the loss--if all crops failed, the farmer could pay for next year's planting with the "cream, hog, and egg" check.

The years after World War I demonstrate a near perfect combination of economic gain, cultural acceptability, and physical possibility of resource development and use. Favorable weather coupled with advances in mechanization took place on a physically favorable milieu, while an economy that had grown on the demand of war needs and the post 1920 national prosperity enabled the High Plains farmer to be gainfully employed. Family farms fulfilled the American dream of land ownership, self-sufficiency, and social

---

[1] No High Plains farmer was ever completely self-sufficient. Maybe the phrase "as close to self sufficiency as we may ever see again" is more appropriate. The farmer of the 1920's had the combination of land, animals, and equipment that could have enabled him to survive longest without outside contact--if by some rare chance he chose to do so.

[2] Class I land, as referred to in this thesis, has less than 1 per cent slope, with fertile clay-loam soils and high soil moisture retention capacity. It is well suited for most crop production when sufficient water is available during an adequate growing season.

approval. It would have been difficult for the resource manager
of that period to foresee that the resource use practices he employed to provide a stable family farm situation would be subjected
to stresses in a hostile environment in the 30's. His failure to
understand and meet the challenge of maintaining long term, renew-
able conservation practices eventually brought tragedy to the
general farming era. It was legally permissible to plow up grassland and to plant and replant soil depleting crops--it was not
only legal, but encouraged. He did not seem to foresee that his
use of resources would be replaced by an economically and physically disastrous combination of resource practices within the next
decade.

Depression, Dust and Crop Failure

Farmers and ranchers on the High Plains had a productive
year in 1930; they planted additional acres of wheat and increased
cattle herds to compensate for the price sag of the 1929 market
crash. As a result grains crowded the market and prices dropped
to 25¢ a bushel for wheat and 12¢ for corn. Grain flooded the
elevators, and farmers bought cattle and hogs to consume their
excess grain. This led to a market glutted with low-priced animals.
Indebted farmers and cattlemen planted every acre in 1931 in an
effort to pay off their creditors; but by March 1932, wind was
gusting daily and precipitation was three inches <u>below</u> normal. Cut
worms invaded corn after a May freeze and crop failure was widespread. Fall wheat[1] was planted everywhere in a futile race

---

[1]Before 1932, spring wheat had been the dominant variety.

between farmer and creditor. In 1933, drought shriveled and killed grain--another crop failure meant more debt. Farmers planted grains in the dust; the topsoil had become like powder--the result of years of "dust mulch" began to be felt. Dust clouds engulfed the region as the strong winds of the spring of 1934 blew daily. By summer, annual precipitation was six inches below normal. Fields were wind-eroded to plow-share depth and the loss of top-soil was immeasurable. Land was abandoned, and those who stayed had the added burden of fighting the drifting dust from deserted fields. Estimates show that one in every three families left the region.[1] It became socially unacceptable and economically diffi-cult to be a "dust" farmer, but many who moved on to California found another unfavorable situation and were known as part of the "Okies" of that generation.

The Agricultural Adjustment Administration of Franklin Roosevelt's New Deal stressed conservation practices. Farmers were paid to practice fallowing, and to list at right angles to the wind, to leave stubble, to strip farm and to plant cover crops. These techniques were ineffective for new crop planting, however, because there was no moisture left to be conserved. Changes in resource practices were too late, and a gainful, possible use of the land appeared impossible.

Locusts swarmed again in 1938, and the government sub-sidized the purchase of poison bait, encouraging farmers to use all they could; and by 1940, locusts seemed under control.

---

[1] Johnson, op. cit., pp. 78-82.

One-Crop Wheat Economy

During the wet spring of 1941, crops and grasses flourished in the Colorado Northern High Plains--for the first time
since 1933. Those who had remained on the land at last earned a
profit. World War II stimulated wheat demand. Throughout the war,
weather cooperated and grain prices were high ($2 a bushel for
wheat even with Office of Price Administration control). Crops
yielded 40 bushels per acre in the better soil areas, and improved
machinery compensated for the loss of war effort manpower. Farmers
who survived the 30's easily netted $30 per acre on wheat land;
before, they had earned less than $200 annually. These few found
the sudden jump in earnings to $5,000-$10,000 a year--a bonanza.[1]

Large land holders (often backed by outside capital)
bought out small holdings. Two or three diesel tractors were a
common sight as they plowed a summer-fallow field of more than a
square mile, or ten self-propelled combines might be used to cut
wheat in an unbroken 150' swath.

Farmers neglected strip and contour farming; again they
began to farm in blocks. The family farm and diversified cropping
prominent in the 1920's did not reoccur. Milking cows, feeding
hogs, or raising chickens were no longer economically gainful for
the family farm. Each unit became specialized, concentrating on
wheat production and occasionally on fattening cattle during the
off growing season. Self-sufficiency disappeared as the farmer

---

[1]Figures estimated from interviews with employees of the
Yuma Consumers Cooperative Association.

depended on the local towns for his consumer needs. But, for perhaps the first time, most High Plains farmers enjoyed a standard of living comparable to urban dwellers. By 1946, a section of wheat land could earn a profit of $4,500 ($9,000 per crop under summer-fallow techniques) and 20 beef cows produced calves that netted another $4,000.[1] Rural electrification, dial telephones, indoor plumbing, air conditioned tractors, and mechanized feed lots made the farmer's life easier and more acceptable. In fact, wheat farming became so efficient that it meant only part-time employment for many farmers. Just two man hours per year, per acre were needed.[2] Once the wheat had been seeded, the farmer need only spray to control weeds and insects, fence the land for winter pasture, and wait and hope that it did not hail.

Consequently, many small landholders developed other interests or jobs to fill their time and purses. They worked or bought businesses in a nearby town, and thus they enjoyed both urban life and rural independence. Farm and home became separate, and many farms were just so many wheat fields, feed lots, and machine sheds.

Land prices rose as Classes I and II land, suitable for wheat, sold for $100 an acre; sandhills grassland and sandy farm land for $40-$50. (By 1965, some of the Class I land was selling for as much as $175 per acre.) Farmers either expanded or sold at

---

[1] Ibid.

[2] Warren Bailey, "Land, Problems in the Wheat Region," Land, the Yearbook of Agriculture, 1958, (Washington, D. C.: U. S. Government Printing Office, 1958), p. 152.

the irresistable prices offered by their neighbors. As farm size increased, population decreased.[1] The cost of living and farm machine prices rose after the war, and it became progressively more difficult for a young man to acquire the capital to begin a farm operation. By 1950, the capital required for 1320 acres (two sections, which is the 1965 average size of farm units in the region) was well over $100,000 for land and another $40,000 for equipment and improvements. Unless the potential farmer inherited the land or went into business with an established farmer (probably his father) the investment was prohibitive.

The apparently stable resource practices that existed in the 1940's faltered as early as 1952 when a dry period occurred. In addition, the national crop surplus situation stimulated government control. Consequently, the practiced resource use was no longer as profitable or practical as before. Government restrictions moved in to place curtailments on the acreage that could be farmed in a particular crop, which, in turn, influenced the farmer to attempt diversified crop types. Twenty five years earlier, as noted previously, diversification promoted a resource practice that for a short time had created prosperity in general farming. But this second attempt of the 1950's could survive only because one or more crops were supported by government subsidies. Subsidization eventually encouraged change in the physical and economic utilization of resources similar to the occurrences at the end of

---

[1]Estimated population in Colorado Northern High Plains in 1940, 45,000; 1950, 38,000; 1960, 29,000; from U. S. Census of Population and Colorado Yearbooks, 1943 through 1962.

the 1920's. Both the 1920's and the 1950's had unstable agricultural environments because at neither time was the resource practice self-sustaining--without either depleting the land or depending on outside aid.

Pump Irrigation

Immediately after World War II a new resource use, pump irrigation, became significant throughout the region. The first irrigation development was along the alluvial deposits of the Republican and Arikaree Rivers, where wells are shallow and low in water production. There were also scattered wells elsewhere. It was not until the mid-1940's that noticeable irrigation development began, and not until the late 40's did the large capacity, turbine-centrifuge type well which pumps several hundred gallons of water per minute become a part of the landscape.

The irrigation "pioneer" in 1945-1950 seemed willing to gamble; he was financially stable but dissatisfied with his current earning situation. The early introduction of pump irrigation was not a response to failure or disaster because the region, on the whole, was relatively prosperous.

In the early 1950's the farm population declined, farmsteads grew larger, but per capita farm income decreased. The cost of living and farm operation were expensive.[1] Then too, the national surpluses of wheat and other grains mounted. By 1953,

---

[1] In Yuma County, individual income in 1955 was down 10 per cent, compared to the cost of living index which was up 10 per cent from a 1947 base. Meanwhile the cost of farm machinery was up 170 per cent from 1948 to 1955.

the Colorado High Plains were committed to agricultural control
and acreage limits. From a regional point of view the full pro-
ductiveness of dryland farming was not legally permissible; sub-
sidized farm markets were available only if acreage controls were
accepted. Yet low precipitation was curtailing farm yields.
Cattle grazing declined because grassland pasture was hindered by
dry weather, even though beef prices were stable in a growing urban
market that demanded more meat to satisfy a high standard of living.
To prosper, a farmer had to make a change in his resource use. So
long as the market price stayed high, rain fell, and hail missed
his farm--he prospered. But a change in any one of these factors
could mean decline and possible failure in his farm system. There
were available certain choices that a farmer could make if he
wanted to improve or maintain a certain standard of living. For
example,

1. He could go into debt and invest in land for a
   larger wheat acreage allotment or expanded cattle
   pasture.

2. He might change the manner and mode of making a
   living in this region; for example, by changing
   from farming to a non-agricultural job. But
   the resource base is suited only for agriculture
   in the present environment and there are few
   practical alternatives.

3. He could sell out and begin again elsewhere (perhaps
   in the city).

4. He could change his farming practices by converting
   or integrating new crops, techniques, or products.

Changes in resource use seemed imminent if farming was
to be economically gainful. By the beginning of 1963, 425 farmers
had installed pump irrigation to this region of dryland agriculture.

This decision outwardly depended on the following:

1. Surpluses of wheat and consequent government controls brought about legal restrictions which limited acreage use. Controls had to be observed for farmers to receive the subsidized market price. Consequently, much land was not planted and became idle.[1]

2. The 1950-1955 drought, although minor when compared to the 1930's, physically restricted dryland grain production and prohibited the limited acreage production from making a satisfactory profit.

3. Technical advances in irrigation equipment enabled the farmer to pump water in quantities sufficient for irrigation.

4. A continuing rise in the market price of beef bolstered a decision to convert to cattle raising; however, drought made the growing of dryland feeder crops difficult. Beef was economically gainful, but it was physically impossible to raise beef cattle without a change in resource practices.

5. Failure of farm income to maintain a level commensurate with national non-farm earnings encouraged the small operator to sell his land. The acquisition of large land holdings by certain operators gave them more potential for credit and an opportunity to acquire financing to change the resource practices.[2]

Those farmers who installed pump irrigation introduced a new response to the environment. Some were successful; others have been only mildly successful; and a few have been economic failures. How the introduction of pump irrigation influences resource development in the Colorado Northern High Plains merits careful analysis.

---

[1]Idle land is culturally unacceptable to most farmers unless it is more economically gainful than "used" land. It is rare when a resource manager will permit land to be idle.

[2]There are sociological implications here as large landholders are considered good long-term credit risks, especially if they acquired their expanded holding via credit. Creditors believe farm land is stable collateral for investment risk.

CHAPTER II

PRESENT RESOURCE USE AND THE POTENTIAL FOR IRRIGATION

An assessment of existing resources is fundamental to
discussing the future of pump irrigation in the Colorado High
Plains. Although the physical landscape is not a determinant of
resource practices in a region, it does constrain the potential
for pump irrigation. An understanding of the relationships that
interact in the environment, thus, is basic to an analysis of the
resource use changes occurring in the study region.

Physical Landscape of the Colorado High Plains

The Colorado Northern High Plains is a site for profitable agriculture when climate and market conditions are favorable.
But variable precipitation means a marginal environment for farming. Hail is frequent, but, fortunately, bumper dryland crops
grown during wet, hail-free seasons offset financial losses of the
adverse crop years. The relatively high fertility of the sandy
loam soils and the gentle, almost imperceptable, slope of the land
allow profitable grain production and cattle grazing when precipitation is adequate and market demand high.

Climatically, the region is semi-arid, but the long term

average annual precipitation of 16 to 17 inches is misleading.

Although the seventy year, 16 inch isohyet passes through the

Colorado High Plains, precipitation for individual years varies

between sub-humid and arid. Figure 2 in Chapter I shows a range

of 9 to 28 inches since 1890 at Yuma, Colorado.[1]

Droughts are common; the longest recorded, continuous

regional drought was from 1931 to 1938. However, most dry spells

end within three or four months and appear localized rather than

regional in extent. These local dry periods seem to be caused by

several months absence of scattered convectional summer thunder

storms or frontal winter snow. Precipitation is best described,

therefore, as locally unpredictable, but not regionally inadequate

for dryland farming.[2]

Mean seasonal temperatures vary from $30^{\circ}F$ in January to

$78^{\circ}F$ in July with characteristic hot, dry days and cool nights in

summer and mild, windy days with cold nights in winter. Continen-

tality produces summer afternoons of $100^{\circ}F$ plus temperatures and

winter nights below zero degrees. But low humidity is typical and

---

[1]Long term averages indicate a late spring, early summer
maximum in precipitation.

[2]Precipitation is mostly convective and frontal in origin
and a result of the condensation of moisture from the infrequent
invasions of "maritime Tropical gulf" air masses. During a 70-
year period yearly maximum and yearly minimums have occurred at
least once during every month. For example, in 1926, May, June,
and July received only a trace of precipitation at Akron, Colorado.
However, August, September, and October received 14 inches of the
19-inch total for that year.
    The area is also invaded by continental Polar, maritime
Polar pacific, and continental Tropical air, but the proximity of
the southern Rocky Mountains and resultant chinook winds coupled
with extreme diurnal radiation make predictions about weather
influences difficult.

has three distinct effects: (1) it causes high moisture loss through evapotranspiration,[1] with little or no moisture retained in soil or surface storage, (2) it aids effective plant growth by the many days of cloudless sunshine to offset the relatively short growing season, (3) it makes the sensible temperature more comfortable than recorded temperatures indicate. Fortunately, the effectiveness of the limited precipitation is increased in years of late spring maximum as this is the period of greatest agricultural need during the 145-day growing season.

The treeless expanse of this steppe land contributes to the moderate and strong winds that sweep the area during all seasons. These winds cause frequent dust storms during dry periods and often pile up the meager winter snow by blizzard drifting. As a result the needed snow moisture for the winter wheat growth is often ineffectively distributed along fence rows or against buildings.[2]

To the eye the land follows a neat, grid pattern of section line fields--a mixture of green rectangles intermingled with brown, fallow land. This is a flat, expansive land whose monotony is broken only by an occasional outlier of grass and "sage brush" covered sand or loess hills which reach into the

---

[1]Evaporation potential tests conducted at Akron, Colorado, reached upper limits of 80 inches per year. (Source: field records, Agricultural Experiment Station, 1926).

[2]The wind factor is quite variable. Farmers complain that windmills have failed to turn for as long as five weeks because the wind was too light.

region from western Nebraska. By season the sequence of color
changes as the spring landscape is dotted with waving green wheat
fields that become golden brown as the grain ripens, then darken to
the color of brown stubble and fallow land by the end of August.
In mid-winter the dusty wheat stubble and parched grass rotate
positions with the newly seeded, brilliant green wheat shoots
which are on occasion covered with winter snow.

Man's Impact on the Colorado High Plains

Man's agricultural activities have greatly altered the
edaphic landscape of the High Plains. Once a rolling plain of
prairie grass developed on nitrogen rich, brown or porous sandy
loam soils, the area is now devoted to commercial production of
winter wheat, livestock, and feeder crops. The natural vegetation
of gamma, crested wheat, and buffalo grasses was plowed under or
grazed. Constant use has broken the original soil structure and
erosion has removed the fine soil particles; severe wind during
the dust bowl of the 1930's transported away much of the topsoil.
Even though it has lost its original sandy loam characteristics,
the soil still produces abundantly when plowed and packed with
modern farm machinery--if it has enough moisture.

Because of the climate, commercial grain crops are
dependent on summer fallow techniques which conserve the precipitation. Dryland feeder crops and grasses survive as best they can
with natural moisture. Surface water for irrigation is either
nonexistent or intermittent and of little use except in isolated
cases.

The Colorado Northern High Plains is now an area of

extensive farming. Farms range in size from about 800 acres to over 2,000 acres (an average of 1,320 acres or two square miles).[1] This extensiveness contributes to isolation as the scattered farmsteads are widely dispersed and stand out as islands of buildings, windmill, shelter-belt trees, and lofty TV antenna. An occupied farmstead may have a modern ranch style house adjacent to a metal quonset for machinery and surrounded by steel grain bins or livestock pens. Many farmsteads have been abandoned since the days of the family farm, and often the building site is nothing more than a storage location of granaries, old barns, and a dilapidated house. Population is spread thinly over the land and concentrates only in the farm-market towns which contain an average of about 1,500 people.[2]

A Changing Regional Scene

The local Colorado High Plains resident is often unaware of a gradual transformation that has taken place in the utilization of land resources. But over a period of years such changes can be identified, and in this area each decade is distinguishable. Fields are now larger and the farms farther apart than they were ten, twenty, or thirty years ago. Today there are many abandoned farms, and the distance to a neighbor's home may be four miles,

---

[1]Rarely, if ever, is the farm a rectangular, two section unit. Usually, the farmscape is spread over an area of up to ten miles and made up of several quarter-section fields.

[2]The small cross-road store or service station of the 1920's has disappeared. Towns that remain are, for the most part, located along the railroads or major highways and serve as market centers, distribution points, county seats, etc. In 1925, there were 47 centers, with a hierarchial range of 4 to 2500 population. Today, 26 remain and of these only 12 could be considered more than a grain elevator and a mere 6 have population of more than 1500.

whereas it was just two or three miles a few years ago. Section line roads, once heavily traveled, are now overrun with weeds and volunteer wheat as they fall into disuse.

Decrease in Population. As farm size grew, population density decreased in the Northern High Plains. Most noteable in the change in resource use is the decrease in the application of human effort to the land. Young people left the farm as they went to college, sought employment elsewhere, and did not return. The post war wheat boom in the late 1940's made it possible for a farmer to offer his children a college education. Also, young men were lured away by the military needs of the Korean police action or by the high wages in urban centers. In 1962, only 13 of the 137 Phillips County graduates in the class of 1950 are now area farmers and only 37 of the class members are still in the region.[1]

Because of the risks and high investment, the land and its operation usually remain in the hands of the established farmer or rancher. In rare cases a son or son-in-law will return to this area to manage a farm, but non-residents have been unable to start a successful farm operation since the days of low interest G. I. loans immediately after World War II.

It is not difficult to ascertain why young residents left the farm. Mechanization satisfied former needs for a large labor force, and the long hours and low wages typical of farm work do not appeal to educated youth. Did the farmer turn to mechanization when he was unable to hire labor, or did he mechanize to

---

[1]Sterling Advocate, editorial, January 17, 1962, estimate by Phillips County superintendent of schools.

replace laborers? Probably the two factors were at work simultaneously.

The Aging Farmer. Enticements to leave the area and limited opportunities within it created a population of middleaged farmers.[1] The area farmer and merchants in the small market towns have grown old together; they have little desire for change. A few young farmers who remained in the area have brought about changes in the agricultural environment. Experiments in truck farming, dairy herds, sugar beets, pump irrigation, etc. have, in general, been tried by farmers under 45. Young men are the main support of the Soil Conservation Service, the county agent, school consolidation, and tax improvements. Recent attempts in Yuma County to obtain sugar beet acreage allotments and the support of the Great Western Sugar Company to develop a sugar beet industry were pushed by a young irrigation equipment salesman and a local Soil Conservation Service agent; both are under 35.

Mechanization and Modern Farming. Machinery does the bulk of the farm work since hired labor and family help have disappeared. Today a wheat farmer can plow in three days[2] an area that took the early homesteader three years or the 1920 farmer three weeks with draft animals. In two days, five men with grain augers, trucks with hydraulic lifts and self-propelled combines can

---

[1]Median age of farmers in Washington County is 54. (Source: Commodity Stabilization Service data, Washington County office.)

[2]This figure does not include the work of summer fallow field preparation.

harvest, deliver, and store the grain from a 640-acre section of wheat. This wheat had been seeded in three to four days by a single man and sprayed in two hours by a two-man team (by plane) for insects and disease. The man hours required for a 640-acre crop totaled less than 100 in 1962. In 1925, more than 2,000 man hours of work were needed to accomplish the same tasks, using a harvesting crew of 25 men.

One rancher, using conveyors, hydraulic hoists, and other automated equipment, can now handle 100 stocker and feeder cattle; plying the animals with vitamins and anti-biotic grain mashes; working faster and more efficiently than five men using pitch-forks and hay racks.

Growth is all that still takes much time. And new seed varieties for crops and scientific feeding for livestock have shortened this period.

Resource Decision-Making in the 1950's

In the 1950's, government controls on acreage and a drought influenced farmers to change resource practices. The summer fallow techniques which had been effective during normal or wet years were of little value when there was no moisture to store. To compensate for reduced acreage, farmers tried to obtain higher per acre yields. Intensive growing techniques such as fertilizing, using special seed grains, and planting more volume to the acre only increased the need for moisture and hastened crop failure during the minor dry periods.

The usual farmer with $100,000 to $200,000 invested in land and equipment had few choices except to expand his land holding to get a larger wheat allotment or to diversify resource practices and in this way to increase his income. Without investing several thousand dollars, there was little hope of establishing truck crop or dairy herds which might compete with areas like the irrigated South Platte Valley. The High Plains farmer had one advantage, land; he could devote greater area to livestock grazing and fattening. If he acquired a stock of feeder cattle, he might develop a competitive feed lot enterprise, providing he could use his land for feed production. Competition was keen; the feed lots of the Colorado Piedmont and the Nebraska Sandhills--based on irrigated alfalfa, sugar beet tops, or sandhill grassland--were already well established. Previously the High Plains rancher had furnished range stock to those established feed lots for fattening. Now, the local farmer who wanted to feed cattle had to find a source of feed crop production to satisfy his own stock. But winter wheat pasture was limited and dryland grain crops were faltering throughout the 1950's.

As the agricultural economy lagged, there was also some searching for non-agricultural income sources. But the area offered little incentive for light industry; oil wells had been dusters; and, except in the Akron area, there was little marketable natural gas. Some alteration of agricultural practices seemed the only practical solution.

Irrigation: an Agricultural Alternative for the High Plains

A physical resource which had lain dormant for the most part was the vast ground water reservoir of the Ogallala Geologic

Formation (Figure 1, Chapter I shows contact zone.) which under-lies the entire Colorado Northern High Plains. Domestic and stock supplies from small diameter wells have not revealed the quantity or quality of available supplies. Ground water is usually found at 140-200 feet, and some municipal wells in the study area supply up to 2,000 gallons per minute (gpm) without depletion. However, in some plains towns well yields are meager and uncertain, making it necessary to move well locations from time to time. This uncer-tainty stimulated an investigation into the extent of the under-ground water supply. If irrigation is to be evaluated accurately as a potential resource use, then a study of the Ogallala as a source of ground water is vital. Could the Ogallala, which under-lies the area, supply a source of water for pump irrigation in sufficient quantities to justify a change in resource use?

When the dryland farmer began to feel the squeeze of government controls, low drought production, and high living costs, he considered well irrigation. If the ground water resource was adequate, three factors that came into being since the end of World War II made irrigation prospectively feasible:

1. Drilling, pumping, and irrigation equipment had been improved so that with a good water supply, 100-160 acres could be irrigated from one well.

2. Power for pumping was available through Rural Electric Association, Low Pressure (bottled) gas, or natural gas.

3. Well financing could be obtained from local or federal agencies who recognized that pump irri-gation had improved the economies of similar areas in west Texas, Kansas, and Nebraska.

Pump Irrigation Potential of the Ogallala Geologic Formation

Water-bearing properties of the Ogallala follow a
pattern typical of heterogeneous unconsolidated aquifers. Its
strata are composed of stream and wind deposits--intermixed
layers of sand, gravel, clay, calachi, shale and silt--that
may transmit water vertically or horizontally. The aquifer
is covered by either Recent dune sand and loess (Figure 3) or
a mature, clay-loam Chestnut and Brown Soil (Figure 4). The
Ogallala rests on an aquiclude of bedrock known as the Pierre
Shale (Figure 5). Pierre is impermeable and permits accumulation of water at the bottom of the Ogallala. Unfortunately,
the top of the Pierre was highly eroded by ancient channels
and does not provide a level bedrock plain. Probably
many of its channels will not be detected until more extensive research is completed. Tables I through VI list the
geologic character of each county in the study area. In several

Figure 3. Sand dune and loessial surface, used mostly for
           grazing.

Figure 4. A shows Class I farm land on mature clay-loam soil. B
illustrates the drilling of an irrigation well into the
unconsolidated Ogallala. Insert in Figure 5 shows pro-
file of the above well core.

34

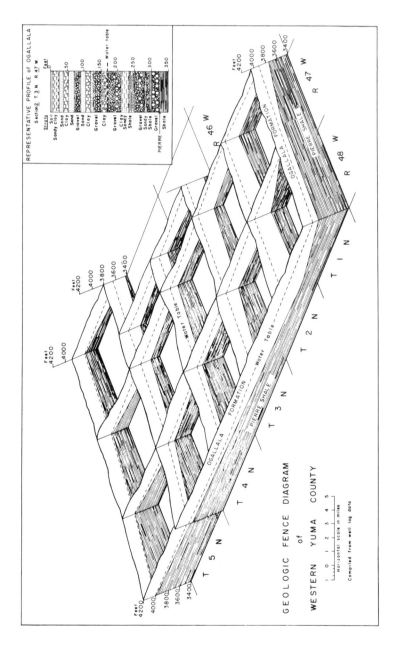

Figure 5. The above diagram is representative of the geologic
situation throughout most of the Colorado Northern
High Plains.

TABLE I.

GENERALIZED GEOLOGIC AND HYDROLOGIC CHARACTER OF YUMA COUNTY

System	Series	Subdivision	Thickness (feet)	Physical Character	Water Supply
QUATERNARY	Recent and Pleistocene	Alluvium	0-75±	Unconsolidated gravel, sand, silt, and clay, both intermixed and as alternating layers	Yields adequate quantities of water for stock and domestic supplies. Alluvium in the valley of the North Fork of the Republican River yields a small quantity for irrigation. Alluvium in the Arikaree River valley yields moderate quantities for irrigation. Alluvium in the valley of the South Fork of the Republican River yields moderate to large quantities for irrigation.
		Dune Sand	0-100±	Tan unconsolidated very fine to coarse quartz sand, wind-deposited	Generally lies above the water table and, hence, yields no water to wells. May yield amounts adequate for stock or domestic purposes where saturated. The dunes are important catchment areas for recharge from precipitation, owing to the relatively high permeability of the sand.
	Pleistocene	Unconformity Peorian loess	0-120±	Yellowish-gray silt and clay containing scattered sand grains and calcareous concretions; wind-deposited	Lies above the water table and, hence, yields no water to wells. Most precipitation runs off. Many intermittent lakes form on the surface.

Source: Colorado Ground Water Basic Data Report No. 2

System	Series	Subdivision	Thickness (feet)	Physical Character	Water Supply
QUATERNARY	Pleistocene	Unconformity Sappe (?) formation	0-10±	Light-gray fossiliferous sand and silty marl overlain by thin soil zone	Generally lies above the water table end, hence, yields no water to wells.
		Grand Island (?) formation	0-30±	Loosely consolidated calcareous reddish-brown to light-gray sand and gravel, stream deposited	Do
TERTIARY	Pliocene	Unconformity Ogallala formation	0-460	Gravel, sand, silt, and clay containing beds of limy sandstone, opaline quartzite, and volcanic ash; "algal" limestone at top; stream-deposited	The principal aquifer in the county. Yields adequate quantities of water for stock and domestic supplies throughout most of area of its occurrence. In many places yields moderate to large quantities for irrigation.
CRETACEOUS	Upper Cretaceous	Unconformity Pierre shale	1,300- 2,500	Gray to black marine shale containing gypsum, bentonite, and calcareous concretions; weathered zone of yellow clay usually present at top	Not known to yield water to wells in the area.

TABLE II.

GENERALIZED GEOLOGIC AND HYDROLOGIC CHARACTER OF WASHINGTON COUNTY

System	Series	Formation	Thickness	Water Supply
QUATERNARY	Recent and Pleistocene	Dune Sand	0-100±	Serves as catchment for recharge but does not yield water to wells
QUATERNARY	Recent and Pleistocene	Alluvium	0-250+	Yields small quantities of water
TERTIARY	Pleistocene	Peorian Loess	0-120+	Yields no water to wells. Occurs above the water table.
TERTIARY	Pliocene	Ogallala	0-385±	Yields small to large quantities of water to wells.
TERTIARY	Oligocene	Chadron	0-300±	Yields small quantities of water from fractures.
CRETACEOUS	Upper Cretaceous	Pierre Shale	2,000-4,500±	Forms the lower confining layer for the water in overlying unconsolidated deposits.

Source: Colorado Ground Water Basic Data Report No. 6.

TABLE III.
GENERALIZED GEOLOGIC AND HYDROLOGIC CHARACTER OF KIT CARSON COUNTY

System	Series	Subdivision	Thickness (feet)	Physical Character	Water Supply
QUATERNARY	Recent	Dune sand	0-10$\pm$	Loose sand, reworked by winds; derived from Pleistocene deposits	Too thin and scattered to be significant as an aquifer; generally above water table.
		Alluvium	0-15$\pm$	Coarse sand and gravel, loose; contains lenses and beds of silt, which are largely reworked loess and windblown sand	A large part lies above the water table. Its main significance is in catchment of precipitation, runoff or stream flow, and temporary storage. It is partly saturated in the upper valley of the South Fork of the Republican River and its tributaries
	Recent and Pleistocene	Dune sand	0-50$\pm$	Coarse silt to coarse sand; poorly sorted. Occurs principally in the stabilized sand hills of the north-central part of the county. Has been reworked in part by winds in Recent time and considerably dissected by streams	Generally above the water table; provides catchment of precipitation for recharge to the ground-water reservoir. Has a fairly high specific yield and moderate permeability.
		Sanborn Group — Bignell formation	0-5	Dark silt, humic in many places	Relatively impermeable, too thin to be significant as an aquifer.
	Pleistocene	Sanborn Group — Brady soil	?	Sandy calcareous silt with roots and fillings	Do

Source: Colorado Ground Water Basic Data Report No. 10.

System	Series	Subdivision	Thickness (feet)	Physical Character	Water Supply
QUATERNARY	Pleisto-cene	Peorian formation	0-50+	Loess; clay and silt-size particles, with minor amounts of very fine sand, compact in most places; generally pale-yellow to pale-brown or tan on the outcrop; principally a windblown deposit, which covers the uplands and forms steep bluffs along some stream valleys	Relatively impermeable; not known to yield water directly to wells. It is significant hydro-logically as a reservoir for soil moisture.
		Sangborn Group — Sangamon (?) soil	?	Buried soil, colored reddish brown by organic material and oxidation; upper part leached of calcium carbon-ate, which is redeposited below as caliche	Not considered an aquifer.
		Sangborn Group — Loveland formation	?	Dark-brown silt. Not definitely identified in surface mapping. Presence suggested by scattered thin deposits in Sherman and Cheyenne Counties, Kansas, and by the thickness of the loess reported on some drillers' logs	Same properties as the Peorian Formation.
		Crete formation	0-10+	Very coarse, rounded to well rounded sand and gravel; par-ticles are not coated with lime. Exposed along the North Fork of the Smoky Hill River and Sand Creek; tentatively identified in test holes and on electric logs	Lies above the water table.

TABLE III. (continued)

System	Series	Subdivision	Thickness (feet)	Physical Character	Water Supply
QUATERNARY		Sappa formation	8 Pearlette Ash	Very fine, pink, pale-purple, and pale-yellowish-gray land, which contains much volcanic ash; shards are unweathered. The hand specimen is light in weight and gritty to the touch.	Not significant except as it affects the quality of water. Ground water in area of outcrop has greater than average concentrations of dissolved solids.
	Pleisto- cene	Meade Group — Grand Island formation	0-50±	Fine to medium, angular, very arkosic, reddish gravel and coarse cross-bedded tan loose sand; upper part contains white calcareous tubular concretions and nodules; locally contains some cobbles. As mapped, it includes some colluvium derived from loess	High permeability and specific yield; locally incompletely saturated. Wells tapping this formation and the Recent alluvium in the upper valley of the South Fork of the Republican River yield 100 to 300 gpm. Yields more than 900 gpm in the valley of the Arikaree River a short distance north of the county line. Wells tapping this formation and the Ogallala Formation have the greatest specific capacities in the county.

TABLE III. (continued)

System	Series	Subdivision	Thickness (feet)	Physical Character	Water Supply
TERTIARY	Pliocene	Ogallala formation	40-50± upper	Algal limestone, tuffaceous waterlaid sandstone, pockets of loose volcanic ash, opalized limestone, chert, dense limestone; fossiliferous in places; toward the base contains sand and gravel, usually cemented	Not significant except as it affects the quality of water; in most areas occurs above the water table; however, water moving through solution openings probably accumulates much of the hardness noted in the underlying ground-water reservoir.
			100-150± middle	Mortar beds, some gray-white, very firmly cemented with calcium carbonate; some pale-pink to tan, much less well cemented, "punky" under the hammer, gritty and light in weight, because of the presence of much volcanic ash (about 5 per cent by volume). Contains fine to coarse arkosic sand, pockets of impure volcanic ash, some loose gravel usually coated with calcium carbonate, limestone lentils, opalized material and opaline chert, and some diatomaceous marl. Contains Testudo, Biorbia fossilia and Celtis willistoni	Incompletely saturated in most of the county. In the western part of the county, locally it tends to confine the water in underlying deposits. The upper part is saturated in the valley of the North Fork of the Smoky Hill River. Affords yields of 300 to 1,000 gpm where the saturated thickness is sufficient. Extensively used for domestic and stock supplies. Probably contributes much of the fluoride concentration in Ogallala waters.

TABLE III. (continued)

System	Series	Subdivision	Thickness (feet)	Physical Character	Water Supply
TERTIARY	Pliocene	Ogallala formation	0-100± lower	Very fine to very coarse loose arkosic gravel in most parts of the area, but locally contains fine to coarse loose sand. Bentonitic clay and silt toward the top. Distribution of coarser materials controlled by valleys cut in bedrock surface. Much less cementing materials than in overlying members; generally gray-white when cemented	Major aquifer; the highest permeability and specific yield. Yields of wells tapping this member and the middle part of the formation range from about 500 to 2,200 gpm. The bentonitic clay may be a source of sulfate and fluoride.
			60± Salt Grass of Elias 1/ member	Gray clay shale; contains many concretions and thin beds of limestone, many with well developed cone-in-cone structure; a few thin betonite beds; abundant septarian limonite concretions; Acantho-scaphites nodosus var, brevis and lucina occidentallis	Most significant as an imperable base for the overlying aquifer. Not sufficiently permeable to furnish much water. A few domestic and stock wills yield very small amounts of rather highly mineralized water from the weathered zone and perhaps from solution openings in limestone lenses.
CRETACEOUS	Upper Cre- taceous	Pierre Shale	200± Lake Creek of Elias 1/ member	Dark-gray and black shale, flaky in places, with many pancake-like concretions, but with cone-in-cone structure rarely well developed. Abundant scales and bones of small fish, Baculites compressus, and Acanthoscaphites nodosus var. quadranqularis. Gypsum very abundant,	Most significant as an imperable base when overlain by the Ogallala Formation of alluvium; probably contributes most of the sulfate concentrations found in waters of the alluvium.

1/ Elias, M. K. 1931

TABLE IV
GENERAL GEOLOGIC AND HYDROLOGIC CHARACTER
OF LOGAN, PHILLIPS, AND SEDGWICK COUNTIES IN FRENCHMAN CREEK BASIN

System	Series	Subdivision	Thickness (feet)	Physical Character	Water Supply
QUATERNARY	Recent	Alluvium	0-100±	Sand, gravel, silt, and clay	Yields large supply along major stream valleys.
	Recent and Pleistocene	Dune Sand	0-170 (?)	Very fine to very coarse sand	Lies generally above water table
		Sanborn formation	0-225±	Tan to brown silt; contains much sand	Generally lies above water table
TERTIARY	Pliocene	Ogallala formation	0-425±	Sand, gravel, clay, silt, caliche; and a discontinuous capping of algal limestone	Yields moderate to large supplies
	Oligocene	White River Group	0-235±	Siltstone, clayey silt, clay and sandstone. May have lenses of quartz sand and gravel near Pierre Shale	The formation, as a whole, is a relatively poor aquifer but locally may yield small amounts
CRETACEOUS	Upper Cretaceous	Pierre Shale	2,650-3,650±	Blue to black clay shale	Yields negligible quantities of water

Source: Modified from Ground-Water Geology and Pump Irrigation in Frenchman Creek Basin Above Palesade, Nebraska, Geological Survey Water Supply Paper 1577.

TABLE V.

GENERAL GEOLOGIC AND HYDROLIC CHARACTER OF EASTERN CHEYENNE AND KIOWA COUNTIES

System	Series	Subdivision	Thickness (feet)	Physical Character	Water Supply
QUATERNARY	Recent and Pleistocene	Alluvium	0-30±	Unconsolidated sand, gravel, and silt	Yields stock and domestic supply
TERTIARY	Pliocene	Ogallala Formation	0-400±	Sand, gravel, clay, clachi with occasional algal limestone caprock	Yields up to 2,200 gpm in some areas. Adequate for stock, domestic and irrigation in most places.
CRETACEOUS	Upper Cretaceous	Pierre Shale	0-1100±	Black to dark-gray shale	Not known to yield water to wells
		Smokey Hill Marl (Niobara)	700±	Gray shaly marl.	same as Pierre

Source: Modified from Geology and Ground-Water Resources in Eastern Cheyenne and Kiowa Counties, Colorado. Geological Survey Water-Supply Paper 1779-N.

areas, particularly along the eastern edge of Yuma, Phillips, and

Kit Carson Counties, the Ogallala is overlain with minor deposits

of Pleistocene and Recent alluvium, loess, and sand. But in terms of

water supply and irrigation potential, only the Pliocene Ogallala

is of prime importance as an aquifer.

United States Geologic Survey hydrologists feel that an

expensive and complex system of test holes would be the only way

to make precise ground water predictions.[1] Because of deep water

levels and intermixed layers, the use of such devices as resistiv-

ity meters is not practical. The Ground Water Division of USGS

has recently begun research on the ground water supply; publica-

tions of those investigations are slowly becoming available.[2]

Present estimates by USGS suggest that there are some 80 million

acre feet of water in storage with 55 million available for use.[3]

---

[1]Information received from United States Geologic Survey
(USGS) was obtained through interviews with personnel of the Ground
Water Division; Federal Center; Denver, Colorado, in 1962 and
1963.

[2]Preliminary basic data reports on the geology and ground
water of Kit Carson, Lincoln, Washington, and Yuma counties are
now available from Ground Water Division USGS, and Colorado State
Water Board; all of these have been or will be followed by water
supply papers. See listing under Boettcher, Cardwell, Chase,
McGovern, and Weist in the bibliography.

[3]This estimate was obtained by computing the total volume
of saturated material times a storage coefficient of 0.15. Volume
of saturated material is depth to bottom of aquifer minus depth
to water table, multiplied by area. Water table contours and
Pierre Shale contours were constructed with information available
from some 450 municipal and irrigation wells plus partial information from 1,500 domestic wells. The storage coefficient was a
standard figure computed for similar aquifers in sedimentation
tank tests. Storage coefficient is that amount of water that
will be released per unit volume of saturated material.

The rest is non-recoverable because withdrawal with compaction of the unconsolidated aquifer traps 25 million acre feet permanently in the lower strata. Only 30 million of the 55 million acre feet lie under irrigable land--therefore, 25 million of the available supply are non-recoverable for irrigation.[1] This water is an accumulation of glacial melt, several centuries of Recent stream flow infiltration, and limited recharge from winter precipitation.

Capillary water in the saturation zone of the Ogallala is in balance between recharge and discharge. The water table slopes gently northeastward, and water probably migrates three to five miles a year in the aquifer. Little new water is added from precipitation. The soil moisture zone is rarely more than three feet deep, leaving 120-200 feet of aerated zone above the water table. (All moisture that falls during the frost-free period is evapotranspirated.) Any vadose water that reaches the zone of saturation must escape the soil zone during periods of frozen ground. Unfortunately, this is the time of least precipitation. It is doubtful that more than one inch of precipitation reaches the water table annually.[2] Some sandy areas or low places that

---

[1] Irrigable land is used synonymously with Class I and Class II land.

[2] Edward J. Farmer ("Colorado Ground Water Problems," Colorado State University Experiment Station, Fort Collins, August, 1959) states recharge in the Ogallala is estimated at .5 to 1.0 inches per year; while USGS estimated .9 inches in Yuma County, .5 in Washington County, 1 inch in Phillips, and 1 to 1.2 inches in Kit Carson County in preliminary well tests conducted during 1958 through 1962. If an estimate of one inch per year is assumed it is sufficient to supply the stock and domestic needs of the area and maintain the balance with the discharge to (Kansas and Nebraska) the east.

fill with water during occasional spring floods may have more recharge, but over the entire area of 10,000 square miles this
represents 640,000 acre feet of recharge. The same amount is
mostly discharged underground to western Nebraska and Kansas. But
despite this discharge, the Ogallala is a vast ground water reservoir and it has definite irrigation potential.

Defining Areas Capable of Pump Irrigation

Not all of the Colorado Northern High Plains has irrigation potential, and some of the area is transitional in both irrigable land and potential water supply. Identification of the area
that can support irrigation is essential to an evaluation of
present development if irrigation is to become a permanent resource
practice.

The initial step taken to identify an area capable of
irrigation was to determine the location of the ground water
supply that permits well development. Hybrid corn, the most
frequently irrigated crop in this region was used as an indicator
of potential crop need in water. This crop requires approximately
25 inches[1] of water at this latitude for maturation.[2] Seventy
year climatic records for Yuma County show that the minimum amount
of precipitation during the driest growing season was approximately

---

[1] The original 25 inches demanded for corn considers evapotranspiration providing the water is not moved more than 3,000
feet on the surface.

[2] Harry F. Blaney, "Climate as an Index of Irrigation
Needs," Water, the Yearbook of Agriculture, 1955, United States
Department of Agriculture, (Washington, D. C.: United States
Government Printing Office, 1955).

7 inches (average was 9.8"). Therefore, an irrigation well must provide up to 18 inches or 1.5 acre feet of water to mature corn. A well pumping 500 gallons per minute will provide approximately two acre feet per day. One field of 160 acres can be supplied by continuous pumping in 120 days. This is marginal at 500 gpm as corn matures in less time, but considering only _minimum_ expected rainfall the two factors should offset each other. Wells, therefore, should supply 120 acres.[1] To locate areas that can supply minimum water requirements, data from 98 irrigation and municipal wells listed systematically by well log code on USGS basic data sheets for Yuma, Washington, and Kit Carson counties or on well logs furnished by Federal Land Bank were studied. All selected wells were used for irrigation (or in the case of municipal wells were of the same type); all have unconsolidated sand and gravel as their major constituents, and all have casings of greater than 12" diameter (median 16"). None has draw down[2] of more than 26

---

[1]Naturally wells which produce more than 500 gpm increase potential acreage up to a certain limit. But land use practices, the range and township system, and transportation distance for water curtail unlimited acreage irrigation. There is little possibility of a well handling more than 160 acres. Farmers will decrease pump time rather than extend irrigated acreage.

[2]Draw down is the lowering of water level that occurs in a well during pumping. While a pump is operating it pulls more water than the infiltration to the casing can supply, as a result the water table is lowered around the pump in the shape of an inverted cone or "cone of depression." This is temporary as long as the original water level can be recovered during the shut off of pump or by increased flow down the sides of the cone. As long as there is sufficient water to infiltrate from surrounding areas, then this is not serious unless the aquifer is so tightly compacted that draw down removes all water and there is insufficient time to recover during shut down. What is more serious is when two or more adjacent wells have cones of depression that coalesce. Then there is little chance for recovery.

feet. Excessive draw down would indicate tighter compaction, less laminar flow, and possible consolidation or a clay lens.[1] The yield range of the 98 wells was from 240 to 2,300 gpm. Mean well depth (also the depth to the impermeable Pierre Shale) was 349 feet; mean depth to water table or contact fringe between zone of aeration and zone of saturation was 169 feet; while the mean yield was 783 gpm. Direct correlation existed between the thickness of the sand and gravel strata in the saturated zone and the water yield in individual wells. From the well logs it became evident that for every foot of sand and/or gravel, the yield was between 5 and 10 gpm. As a cross check, the mean thickness of sand and gravel was computed for all 98 wells; this was 69 feet. If 69 feet yielded an average 783 gpm, then 50 feet should yield 558 gpm. It was noted that when well logs showed 100 feet thickness of sand and gravel, the yield was more than 1,000 gpm. Therefore, in order to establish realistic yet broad limits for the region, the following generalization is made: All areas of 50 ft. of saturated, unconsolidated sand and gravel are expected to yield a minimum of 500 gpm (Figure 6). The following estimates were developed as a basis for delimiting the potential yield areas.

Thickness of Aquifer (50% must be unconsolidated sand and gravel)	Yield
0 - 50 ft.	less than 500 gpm
50 -100 ft.	500 - 750 gpm
100 -200 ft.	750 - 1000 gpm
200 -300 ft.	1000 - 1500 gpm
300 -400 ft.	more than 1500 gpm

---

[1]For the purpose of this analysis, draw down is assumed to be a constant because these data are used later for undeveloped areas and draw down is not actually measurable until a well has been drilled.

50

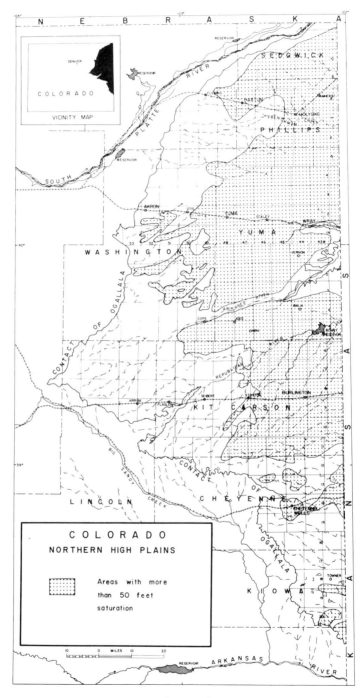

Figure 6

For general use and ease of application, 50 feet of saturated, unconsolidated material is expected to yield a minimum of 500 gpm. Areas of 50 or more feet of saturated sand and gravel were identified by using logs from the 98 well locations discussed above.

The index for potential water use in the Colorado Northern High Plains has, therefore, been established at 500 gpm. The next step was to locate those areas capable of producing 500 gpm and this involved plotting the difference between depth to water table and depth to bedrock for wells that have 50 ft. or more of saturated sand and gravel. The result was a choropleth map (Figure 7) showing the various zones of width of saturated sand and gravel. These zones were then correlated with known well production, and yield potential was matched with the various zones on the map.[1]

Employing a Department of Agriculture Land Use Map (Figure 8) and additional field work, maps of irrigable land and sufficient available water were combined (Figure 9). This map shows the various land classes that are underlain with 50 feet or more of saturation.

An area that has sufficient ground water but is not suitable for irrigation is the sandhills. This eolian dune sand is an outlier of the Nebraska Sandhills Province. Despite its high porosity, infiltration, and percolation, its coarse textured

---

[1]The correlation method was more simple to compute than the technique used by USGS, using transmissibility and storage coefficients which established approximately the same results. However, its reliability outside the Ogallala would require testing.

52

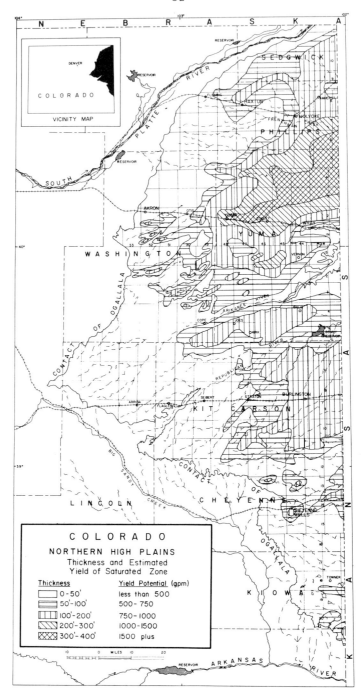

Figure 7

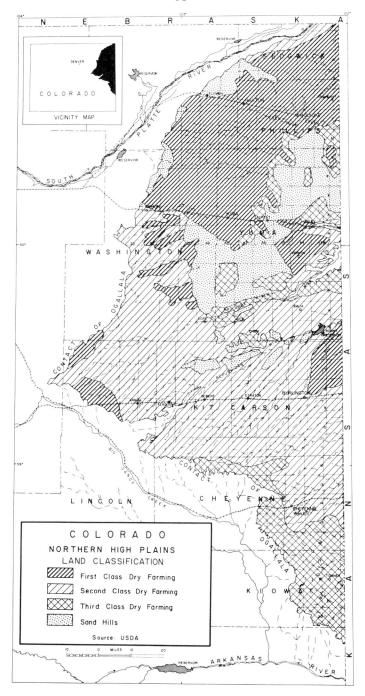

Figure 8

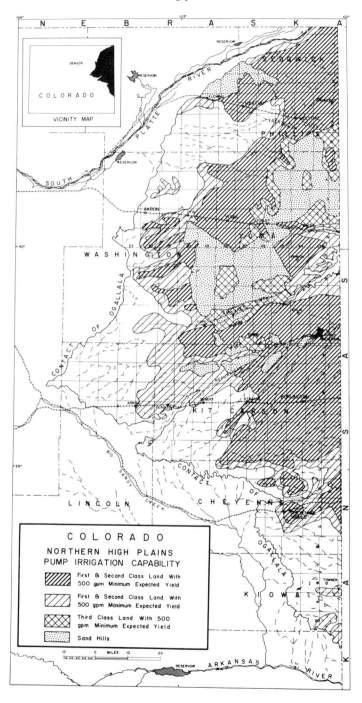

Figure 9

soils and irregular topography prevent it from serious considera-

tion for irrigation development. Infiltration rate is so high

that water applied does not remain in the soil zone long enough

to be used for irrigation. Consequently, this means that an area

of more than 1,300 square miles with good water supply has to be

rejected. (Figure 3)

Class I land with less than 1 per cent slope, fertile

clay loam and sandy loam soils, and high water retention, covers

more than 3,000 square miles of the 50 ft. saturation area. Here

is the greatest potential for ground water resource development.

This land is some of the richest grain producing farm acreage.

(Figures 4 & 13) Fringing this area is another 1,170 square

miles of Class I land with marginal water potential for 500 gpm.

Wells in this sector may have capability of 500 gpm, but the

duration of yield is limited because of a narrow zone of satura-

tion. Most Class II and Class III land has more than 500 gpm

potential (understandably, because this is generally the transi-

tion between Class I and dune sand). Therefore, it has more

porous soil and a higher rate of recharge. These lands are too

sandy and have little potential for future irrigation.[1]

Summary

Not only has there been change in the resource practices

---

[1]Not all of the present irrigation wells are in the 50
ft. saturation zone. However, those outside this zone are in
stream bed alluvium and pump from a combination of Recent deposits and Tertiary sandstone of the Ogallala (which is too narrow
to show on the map). These wells are shallower, less productive,
and many are showing signs of extensive draw down and water depletion.

in the Colorado Northern High Plains, but this region has potential
for still another resource use adjustment. Irrigation is physically possible. Physical ability, however, cannot guarantee the
innovation and growth of an agricultural practice. When the individual farmer converts part of his operation to pump irrigation,
he encounters a host of problems. He ponders whether such a
change in resource use will be gainful, acceptable, and permissible.
He must make important adjustments in farming techniques, equipment needs, labor requirements, etc. The non-irrigator who wants
to change his use of the resource base to increase his income
watches with interest to see if his neighbor's irrigation venture
will be profitable. The addition of pump irrigation to the
economy of the High Plains involves much more than acquiring a
productive well.

CHAPTER III

DEVELOPMENT OF PUMP IRRIGATION
IN THE NORTHERN HIGH PLAINS OF COLORADO

The decision to complement a dryland farming system by installing an irrigation well involves more than ascertaining the availability of water. Irrigation creates a new land use; it is not a device to supplement yield of present dryland crops, but a challenge for the farmer to combine two farming techniques under one general operation. Development involves several economic and social considerations. Farm management must change, and as old problems are solved new ones are created. The farmer is faced with decisions on location, financing, installation, land use, and crop type, as well as the influences of the change on family, tradition, attitudes and opinions. Regardless of the advantages or disadvantages, by the beginning of 1963, 425 farmers had installed 435 irrigation wells in the Colorado Northern High Plains.

Description of Expansion

The first irrigation well recorded in the Colorado Northern High Plains was installed in 1935. Pump irrigation might have spread rapidly in the dust bowl of the 30's, but the depressed economy and lack of proper equipment impeded development. The technology of ground water pumping was not sufficiently

57

sophisticated to attract large scale financing except in certain municipal areas where the local governments could afford the expensive, cantankerous pumps. By 1940, there were just ten irrigation wells in the entire study area; these were shallow and generally drilled in the alluvial deposits along Frenchman Creek near Holyoke or in the Arikaree and Republican River banks of southern Yuma County. Early wells could not supply enough water unless the depth to saturation was shallow and the aquifer dominately gravel. A centrifugal-centripetal type pump with high volume yield, self-lubrication, and sand rejection was not generally available, except in costly experimental models. But there was no credit available to finance a conversion to irrigation even if equipment had existed. World War II curtailed development of pump irrigation, and during that time dryland crops flourished as precipitation was adequate. Farm machinery was scarce and because conversion to irrigation demanded additional equipment, there was little possibility of this change in resource use.

Rate of Installation

An increase in pump well installations came in 1948 (Table VI). Previously an average of two new wells were installed each year; but in 1948, nineteen wells were drilled. Since that time wells have been drilled on the average of 25 per year--ranging from 10 to 80 during individual years. Figure 10 shows the irrigation wells per township in 1948. Wells which existed then are about 10 per cent of the present number and are considered as the base for the study of irrigation. Figure 11 illustrates the number of irrigation wells installed per township by the end of

TABLE VI.

YEARLY WELL INSTALLATIONS IN THE NORTHERN COLORADO HIGH PLAINS

Year	Wells Installed	Accumulation
1935	1	1
1936	1	2
1937	3	5
1938	1	6
1939	0	6
1940	4	10
1941	2	12
1942	2	14
1943	0	14
1944	1	15
1945	2	17
1946	2	19
1947	3	22
1948	19	41
1949	29	70
1950	17	87
1951	14	101
1952	14	115
1953	18	133
1954	34	167
1955	80	247
1956	42	289
1957	30	319
1958	10	329
1959	19	348
1960	18	366
1961	31	397
1962[1]	6	403
1963[2]	32	435

[1] 1961-1962 totals were acquired from local sources but registry will move several of the 1961 wells into the 1962 line. Total accumulation is correct.

[2] Well installation in 1963 is an estimate taken for local sources and is not the official registry at the Office of the State Engineer. Although contracted in 1963 for installation, most of these wells will not operate until the summer of 1964. Installation of irrigation wells usually occurs in the winter or off-growing season, as the innovator has more time to devote to the purchase, contracting, bartering, and supervision of the well installation. However, the State Engineer legally requires annual logging of wells (with over 3"diameter) in the Denver office; consequently, a well recorded in 1959 may have been drilled in the autumn of 1958, etc.

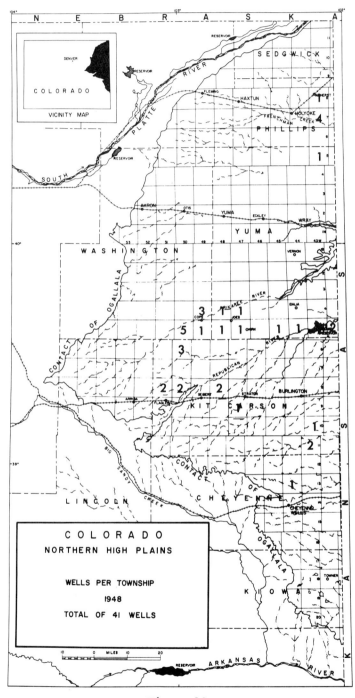

Figure 10

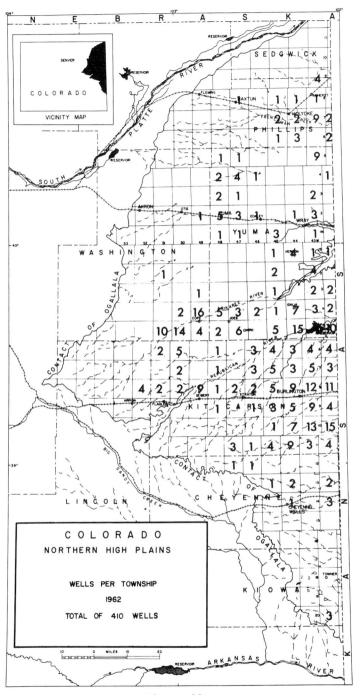

Figure 11

1962; these were in operation at the beginning of the 1963 growing season. Figure 12 presents the actual location by dot of
individual wells.

Other factors establish 1948 as the base year for post
war change in water resource use. Technology made important advances during the industrial expansion of World War II. Wells
could be equipped with turbine pumps which have a mixed flow type
turbine that combined the characteristics of earlier centrifugal
and propellar type pumps. Turbines were oil or water lubricated
and could eject foreign particles such as sand, without damage
to the pump during high velocity, high volume pumping. These
pumps were efficient and required little maintenance or repair.
Also, by 1948, the production of farm machines for civilian use
began to recover as factories converted back from war production.
A wide variety of new machines for dry and irrigated farming was
available.

By 1963, this 10,000 square mile area, two thirds of
which is productive farm land, is but beginning to be irrigated
with 435 wells. Less than 4 per cent of the potential irrigable
land is being irrigated by 10 per cent of the farm operators on
the land.[1] However, it is significant that pump irrigation is
increasing.[2] Figure 13 visualizes this new contrast.

---

[1]Less than 1 per cent use is solely as a method of crop
production.

[2]Pump irrigation is not spreading rapidly, nor do most of
the present well owners believe that it will. In a survey of 60
irrigators in this region, 85 per cent answered "yes" to the statement, "Irrigation will spread, but not rapidly," Only 13 per cent
thought, "It's going to grow very rapidly," while the remaining
2 per cent predicted no increase.

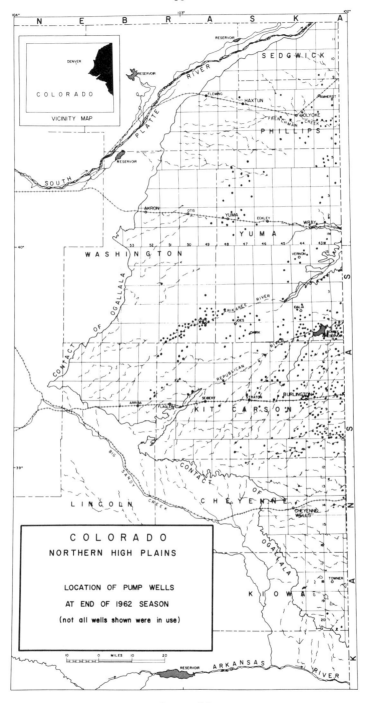

Figure 12

Figure 13.   The three major contrasting land uses: cattle grazing,
winter wheat, and irrigation.

Land Use Change Due to Irrigation

Corn occupies the largest amount of irrigated land. Plots average 70 per cent in hybrid corn, 20 per cent in sorghums, and 10 per cent in clover, alfalfa or some form of truck crops. A few irrigators are experimenting with sugar beets in scattered areas, but irrigated sugar beets are in a state of uncertainty at the present time, as sugar beet quotas fluctuate at government levels.[1]

Truck crop potential is limited in this region. Distance from market, lack of harvest equipment, absence of available "stoop" labor, etc., would make conversion to truck farming a speculative venture with scant assurance of profit. As this area is frequently pelted by intense hail storms, the high investment in items such as celery and tomato seedlings would be extremely risky.

Corn, therefore, dominates the irrigated land in the Colorado Northern High Plains because of its high yield and demand as livestock feed, and it will probably remain the leading irrigated crop for many years.

---

[1]Sugar beets would not change the installation, management, or fuel requirements but would reflect in the land use and machinery needs. The cost and benefit would not be greatly altered except that beets offer a less competitive and more tightly controlled program than feed crops. With the increase of sugar quotas after the 1962 Cuban crisis, domestic production potential rose. Kit Carson County produced several tons of sugar beets in 1962 and 1963, and irrigators in Yuma County are committed to 650 acres of irrigated beets with price guarantee from Great Western Sugar Company in the summer of 1964.

Irrigated corn produces 60 to 100 bushels per acre.[1]
Several farmers have reported yields of more than 120 bushels per
acre during the past six years, but most of these have been intensive cases of constant irrigation and management control. At
least ten irrigators out of sixty interviewed admitted they
neglected their irrigated corn fields during the two to three
week, labor-critical wheat harvest in July because they were too
busy, although this was a crucial time for cultivation and water
application. This neglect during the hot, dry period can easily
cut yields of irrigated corn by 20 to 30 bushels or stunt budding
sorghums several feet.

Corn is grown for both cattle feed and the commercial
market; whereas, sorghums and alfalfa are generally grown only
for feed, and sugar beets only for resale. More than two-thirds
of sixty irrigation farmers interviewed report that irrigated
crops fed to cattle are usually between 50 and 80 per cent of the
total irrigation production. Many of the farmers hope to enlarge
cattle feeding enough to use all of their irrigated crops. Thirty
eight per cent of the interviewed farmers said they would prefer
to expand their present irrigation crop rather than expand their
present dryland crop acreage operation; while 25 per cent would do
the opposite. The rest chose other alternatives or would not expand at all. But 88 per cent of the total would like to add or
expand their cattle feeding regardless of whether or not they

---

[1]Compared to dryland corn which yields 12 bushels per
acre on the average. Colorado, 1961-1962 Yearbook, State Planning
Division, Denver, Colorado.

expanded irrigation, dry farming, or chose not to expand crop
production.

Some farmers have considered the possibility of sheet
flooding winter wheat and pasture grasses as an alternative, but
so far it is not practiced. The extensiveness of the planted
acreages and the sensitivity of wheat to rot are definite limitations. In all irrigation there is a tendency to use ditch and
furrow distribution of water; however, there are many wells
equipped with both gated pipe and sprinkler systems. Individual
preference about distribution systems prevails rather than areal
preference.

A few attempts have been made to establish dairy farms
supported by irrigated feed crops. Several factors have limited
this potential land use: (1) the widely dispersed farms and irrigation wells create expensive transportation for any "milk route,"
(2) the centralizer belt described by Loyal Durand[1] in the 1940's
is almost non-existent; it passed with the family farm, (3) market
competition is keen as the Colorado Piedmont has developed dairy
herds to handle the Denver area, and (4) state dairy laws require
stringent control and sanitation facilities that boost conversion
costs as much as 40 per cent over activities such as beef feeder
pens.[2]

---

[1]Loyal Durand, Jr., "American Centralizer Belt," Economic
Geography, 31: 310-320, 1955. The centralizer belt described an
area outside the traditional dairy regions where the farmer milked
cows as a secondary source of income and sold the separated cream
to central locations for shipment to butter producing plants.

[2]A limited amount of dairying was encouraged in 1963 when
a cheese processing factory in the Denver area started a "route"

Economics of Pump Irrigation

The individual who ponders irrigation adoption is primarily concerned about its ability to make money for him. Uncertainty about financing, credit availability, costs, and net gains are uppermost in the mind of any innovator. Rarely has any farmer in the High Plains had the money for a cash outlay when he converted to irrigation.

Installation Requirements

The initial pump irrigation problem involves location and installation of the well pump unit. Outside the Sandhills area, the topographic gradient is rarely more than 20 feet per mile; therefore, there are no poor choices of land slope. Soil type seldom varies within an individual farm unit, so it is not of primary concern (assuming the farmer considers only Class I land—which is usually the case). In a study conducted by the author in western Yuma County in 1961,[2] the general reasons for the decision for a given well location were found to be: (in order of importance) (1) land with the best quantity water tests by test holes, (2) land nearest the power source, such as natural gas or rural electric lines, (3) land close to the farmstead or feed lots, or (4) land with the lowest government wheat acreage allotment.

The water resource itself is usually not a paramount

---

to acquire milk for cheese. Dairy laws are more liberal in controlling this type of milk, but so far this outlet is being used by only a few farmers who want some employment during the off-growing season.

[2]Leonard W. Bowden, "Pump Irrigation in Western Yuma County: An Environmental Adjustment." Unpublished Masters Thesis, University of Colorado, Boulder, 1961.

factor, once the farmer has decided to install a well. Although

he rarely has an accurate idea of the quality or quantity of the

ground water, he often makes judgments by watching the performances

of surrounding wells or coordinating location with his most suc-

cessful domestic well. As a result, there are few "dusters,"

because most farmers outside the yield area simply do not bother

to gamble on an expensive but untested well installation.

Drilling an irrigation well is expensive. Because of

the high yield necessary, the diameter of the hole and its casing

must be at least 12" and usually is 16-18".[1] Although the mean

depth to water is approximately 150 feet, almost all wells are

drilled to the impermeable layers of the Pierre Shale aquiclude,

taking advantage of as much saturated zone as possible. Normal

costs of well drilling are about 20^{\pm}$ per foot, and under favor-

able conditions 70 to 100 feet can be drilled in ten hours. The

entire operation, which consists of setting up a rig, drilling

test holes, drilling the well hole, installing perforated and

solid casing, connecting equipment, and making well tests requires

about ten days. However, the physical character of the Ogallala

makes it impossible to determine exact cost or installation time

of the drilling operation in advance.

A cost breakdown for 15 well installations between 1955

and 1960 reveals an average expense of $4,440 for the well and

$6,650 for motor and pump, or an overall average cost of $11,090

---

[1]Minneapolis-Honeywell irrigation charts confirm that
increase in diameter over 18 inches does not seem to increase
yields proportionately.

per well. (Minimum was $8,800 and maximum, $14,000). Rising equipment and labor costs have advanced this average figure to almost $14,000 in 1964.[1]

Because the innovation of irrigation means a change in crop type and intensity of land use, it also requires the acquisition of different types of farm equipment. In addition to equipment for ditching, pipe trailers, land levelers, and sprinklers, the installation of a well demands small, row-crop type machinery. The large, extensive farm equipment used for dryland farming is not compatible with the intensive cultivation of irrigated crops. New storage facilities for irrigated crops, different fuels for the new pump or machinery, etc., all add to the initial installation financial burden.

During interviews with irrigators, all complained about the initial high cost. And, as irrigation is secondary to almost 90 per cent of the well owners, it means they have costs of dryland equipment and operation in addition to the costs of irrigation. Machinery and farm implement salesmen in both Yuma and Kit Carson Counties estimated the total cost of getting the well installed and purchasing adequate and additional equipment at between $25,000 and $30,000 without operating or maintenance costs. It is understood, of course, that if the land had to be purchased as well, it would raise the total costs to $45,000 for a 160-acre irrigation plot.

---

[1] Information taken from Federal Land Bank well installation logs for Washington and Yuma Counties.

Operation and maintenance expenditures of a pump unit vary and depend on the type of fuel used. Those operating on natural gas can be used and maintained for approximately 30¢ per hour, while butane and diesel fuel are slightly less than $1 an hour, and electric units operate for about $1.20 per hour. An average pumping season is 1,250 hours.[1] However, electric pump units have a much greater longevity--as long as 30 years without major repairs. Although natural gas is the cheapest fuel, it is only available near the town of Burlington and along the rail line that passes through Yuma. Many farmers have purchased butane operated engines and suggest that this may have been influenced by the possibility of future expansion of natural gas lines and the ease of conversion of their units.[2]

Financing and Credit

Well financing has generally been handled by the Farm Home Administration (FHA), Federal Land Bank system, or by local bankers. Several wells in Kit Carson and Phillips Counties have had FHA support, but in Yuma County the greatest supporter has been Federal Land Bank.[3] Because FHA offers the lowest interest

---

[1]Computed from fuel records receipts, Colorado-Nebraska Natural Gas Company.

[2]In 1963, a local gas company in Kit Carson County proposed installation of gas lines to wells within ten miles of Burlington. Although still largely in the planning stage, it was the first indication of a supplier of power showing interest in the potential market of irrigation fuel. Y-W Electric Association began an advertising campaign in Yuma and Washington Counties to "educate" potential irrigators to the advantage of electric motors for pump wells.

[3]The Federal Land Bank System is under the supervision of the Farm Credit Administration but is entirely farmer owned. Farm Home Administration uses appropriated federal government funds and offers supervised credit service to family-type farms.

and longest term loans, it is most desirable. However, each county is under the control of a different evaluator whose judgment determines whether a particular area is suitable for loans. The more liberal the county evaluator, the more wells FHA supports. The influence of this loan situation may be significant in that FHA will only finance a potential well that it believes will be self-sufficient. One FHA agent argues that he is against allowing loans because he suspects many wells are being supported by income from dryland crops.

Federal Land Bank and other financing organizations will support well installation if the farmer's credit or collateral are satisfactory. In other words, they will support the addition of an irrigation well to a farm operation as long as they are assured the previous dryland activity will be continued or that the individual is capable of withstanding a failure in his irrigation enterprise. Although each situation is different, the general trend is to finance half or two-thirds at 5 to 7 per cent for five, ten, or fifteen years. (FHA rates can be as low as 4.5 per cent, with up to 40 years and three-fourths of the enterprise covered.)

Irrigation Well Income

An irrigator in Yuma County offered detailed information on what six years of irrigation had cost and how much profit he had made. (See Table VII) This breakdown is probably the most representative available because the operation was not logged as part of an overall farm enterprise. At the end of ten years the unit would be paid for and should have another 15 years of service.[1] If his land had been mortgaged ($150 per acre without well for twenty years at 6 per cent) or if his crops were destroyed two or three years by hail, his profit would have been cut almost in half. Another factor that interfered is the government "feed grain program" that began in 1960. If allotted acreage were cut 30 per cent, the proportionate cut in profit would be more than half due to his higher production cost and despite support price, unless he found a secondary outlet such as feeder cattle. However, this farmer believed that his well was a better investment than buying another quarter section of wheat land ($22,000) and trying to produce two quarter sections of dryland crops.

TABLE VII.
INDIVIDUAL WELL COST AND INCOME*

Item	Cost	
Well and Equipment Cost	$20,000	
Fuel Cost and Operation Expense	$1.00	per hour
Interest on Loan	$360	per year (one-half of well cost financed)
Cost of Planting and Fertilizing	$22	per acre/year
Taxes	$340	per year
Market Value of Product	$1.00	per bushel
Hours of Well Operation	1,200	per season
Labor in Actual Well Operation**	200	hours per season
Yield per acre (corn)	70	bushels (5-year average)
Irrigated Acreage	140	acres
Yearly Expenses	$6,780	
Gross Income	$9,800	
Net Profit	$3,020	

*Figures are rounded off to nearest tenth.
**Does not include land and machine preparation during off-pumping season.

[1]This does not consider the difference in profit between irrigated and former dryland crops which will be pointed out later in the chapter.

Similar production to that used by the individual farmer just described is typical of most of the irrigated projects, but results vary because farmers feed half or more of their crops to their own cattle. Although Table VII considers an individual, each farmer has much more to contemplate than one system. He must ponder if his decision to irrigation will eventually replace his dryland operation, supplement it, or maintain it.

Adding Irrigation: Economic Gain or Loss

Farmers select resource practices and systems that they believe will give them the highest net profit. The Colorado Northern High Plains has traditionally been a "boom or bust" situation for agriculture; a situation brought about by unpredictable weather more than any other influence. By mid-twentieth century, however, multiple hazards are shaping the attitudes and opinions of farmers who desire changes in resource use. Along with unreliable weather, farmers are faced with fluctuating prices, a surplus market, inconsistent government programs, limited knowledge of resource potential, and other factors of risk and uncertainty.

Farmers' attitudes toward risk vary with their financial positions and ages. A young, indebted farmer with a growing family is under pressure for immediate income; the older, established farmer is usually interested in steady, long-term income that will support his retirement. A man whose reserves are meager cannot afford to take many risks, perhaps including pump irrigation. Low annual income or lack of adequate capital can force a farmer to invest what he has for a quick return--an easily liquidated farming system. Conversely, a farmer with good collateral and credit who might establish pump irrigation may be reluctant to give up present income for an investment that because of present value[1] will mean great future income possibilities. The established, middleaged farmer without the responsibilities of a growing family has little incentive to speculate for future wealth.

Both winter wheat and livestock raising can fulfill the minimum income demands of most farmers. Livestock, though costly to initiate, can be liquidated quickly should income be needed. Winter wheat requires a low investment and offers a reasonably quick return. Even though the agricultural environment is, in general, hazardous,[2] with summer-fallow rotation, stubble mulching, controlled grazing on natural and winter wheat pasture, and use of pesticides there is scant soil depletion, overgrazing or erosion. To the High Plains farmer, wheat and cattle offer certain advantages as a farming system. With such a system the farmer does not have to save acreage for spring feed crops such as sorghums, barley, millets, etc. He may plant all permissible acreage in winter wheat and leave his remaining land fallow. Then, should some of his winter wheat crop fail, spring crops can be planted on the fallow land. He may on occasion even plow up a poor stand of

---

[1]The value of a sum of money due at a future time is called the present worth or present value of that sum.

[2]Hazards, as used here, are those variable elements that disturb an expected agricultural production. They are generally unpredictable such as diseases, hail, drought, sudden drops in market price, etc. Hazards have minimal effect on long-term investment but are particularly critical in marginal physical and/or economic situations.

wheat and plant an alternate crop such as fast maturing hershey. This is possible because the wheat seeding investment is low per unit of land.

Irrigation does not offer the flexibility of winter wheat and cattle grazing.[1] An irrigation system utilizes intensive cropping at high investment per unit of land. Consequently, it demands a cropping system that yields high income. A pump well and its auxiliary equipment are fixed assets and an integral part of the capitalization of the farm. To be economically attractive, therefore, irrigation must increase the overall efficiency and stability of the farming system and increase the present worth of the investment; it must prove more desirable than comparable investment elsewhere.

Irrigation lowers the degree of risk or hazard from weather in this semi-arid climate, and it will also increase yields per acre and add to the diversity of the overall cropping system. The irrigator is assured a reasonable annual income[2] and, therefore,

---

[1] A significant factor concerning irrigation is the immobility of the pump well; it cannot be rotated or shifted to another field. Because it is located on a specific plot, that field will receive the most attention and use--probably yielding the most profitable crop.

[2] For example, if a farmer sells half his irrigated crop for a $1510 net profit and feeds half to his cattle, he can raise the expected net income of $1800 per quarter section for cattle to $3600 because he can support twice as many cattle per acre with supplemental feed. Even if forced to liquidate half his herd during a drought, he can still realize $3310. Without a well his profit would be $2850 from the same land under a wheat-cattle system when no weather hazard is considered--much less when it is.

can do more long-term planning. He can shift operating costs[1] to
a fixed capital asset thus acquiring potential collateral for
obtaining long-term loans, stability, and the appearance of a permanent enterprise.

A hypothetical economic example of the pros and cons
involved in a decision to convert to irrigation might be as follows:
In 1962, a 100-acre irrigated corn field netted approximately
$3100 compared to a wheat field of comparable size which netted
$1050--a difference of $2050 (This does not consider the wheat
weather hazard). If the investment for irrigation conversion was
$25,000 for this acreage, then how long would it take for the
farmer to realize an increase in the value of his irrigation investment over that in his wheat crop? With the present worth of
10 annual incomes of $2050 (at a 5 per cent discount rate), the
difference in net profit from the two crops, is about $15,500 and
the present worth of 20 annual incomes of the same amount is
approximately $25,500. An investment in irrigation becomes more
profitable than dryland wheat after 20 years of operation. If,
realistically, the risks in dryland farming are considered and
proper management of the irrigated enterprise impedes serious
erosion and soil depletion, then the breakthrough to higher profit

---

[1]Long-term operating costs will increase, although well
depreciation will decline with age as land deterioration accelerates on the well location. Farmers are already feeling the effects
of gully and sheet erosion in some irrigated fields, and although
this is due to the experimental stage, the situation does not
appear to be improving. Many fields that were hastily levelled,
improperly graded, and poorly prepared are showing signs of severe
water erosion and soil leaching. Land preparation, even in this
plains area, costs up to $80 per acre--an expense some irrigators
try to avoid.

taking probably occurs about 15 years after well installation. Should a lower interest rate be available, the present value figure would become favorable in less than 15 years.

With this in mind, thirty irrigators were asked, "How many years do you estimate it will take for your well to pay for itself (consider the money you could have made under dryland farming of the same land)?" Seven said less than 5 years (24%), another seven said between 5 and 10 years, but eleven estimated more than 10 but less than 20 years. The remainder felt at least 20 years, but no one thought more than 30 years. One irrigator commented, "Nobody should put in a well that can't pay for itself in 10 years." But, in general, the answers revealed that most would not have ventured into irrigation if it were not believed to be profitable in less than 20 years.

In practice, financial return is not the only factor which influences the decision to convert to irrigation. Other considerations include the probability that: (1) part of the income from wheat crops is used to pay off the irrigation investment so that profits can be realized sooner, indirectly increasing the present value of irrigation, (2) rarely is the entire investment for pump irrigation financed: a portion is usually purchased from operating capital or savings, these too, eventually raise the present value of the irrigation investment. In practice, an established farmer who has available credit or cash to invest must decide which of several courses is most gainful for him. In a survey of thirty-five irrigators who were asked, "If you had $40,000 and your choice of the following, which would you do?"

(Choices offered are of comparable value.), replies were as
follows:

    Buy a quarter section of good land with a 1,000 gpm well 38%
    Buy two quarters of good wheat land and not irrigate   28%
    Buy a section of Sandhills grassland for grazing   14%
    Sell present operation and invest elsewhere or retire   20%

Thirteen farmers who live next to irrigators but do not irrigate

themselves responded: four in favor of the first choice and the

remainder would take one of the remaining choices.

    There are interesting comparisons in the compound inter-

est (5%) on profits from the four alternatives in the above ques-

tion. Using a $40,000 investment, the profits outlined in Table

VIII could be anticipated if present value of 1963 market prices

remains consistent.[1] Each choice had advantages and the ultimate

decision must be a selection that best fits individual needs,

farming system, goals, and abilities of the farmer.

    A successful farmer manages each portion of his enterprise

to achieve a profitable combination and balance in crops and live-

stock. The addition of pump irrigation will affect that balance

and alter the entire farm operation. Figure 14 illustrates the

apparent relationship for a future combination of dryland farming,

---

[1]Labor costs are not considered because in practice
these are one-man operations. Once a salaried employee or manager
is involved, the entire costs structure would result in a 2% or
less profit. This would mean then more land, higher yields, and
scientific farming would be necessary to compensate the self-
employed (single) farmer. The larger enterprises can operate on
narrow margins. For example, the corporate farm invests in expensive machinery that may be used almost 90% of the time. On an
individual enterprise particular machinery is idle a good deal of
the time. In a few instances two neighbors may go into partner-
ship on machinery such as a self-propelled grain combine which
costs $9,000. The combine is used a maximum of two weeks by its
owners.

TABLE VIII.

PROFITS FROM COMPARABLE $40,000 INVESTMENTS

	wheat	irrigated corn	grassland	other[1]
one year	$ 3,100	$ 3,800	$ 2,800[2]	$ 2,100
ten years	$ 48,900	$ 61,900	$ 45,600	$ 32,600
twenty years	$161,200	$192,800	$257,600	$104,000

livestock husbandry, and supplemental irrigation. The slope of
the curves considers the present worth of future amounts of income and cost. This graph shows the overlap of the gain and loss
in the three system operation. The beef and irrigated corn investments depend on each other as irrigated corn reduces the
(drought) hazard of beef cattle. Lines A', B', C' and D' show
total income (black) in contrast to total cost (white). This
graph cannot fit individual situations, but it is a generalization
for the regional pattern. The system here represents a owner-
operated wheat farm with supplemental beef cattle. The initial
high cost for irrigation installation and equipment and the high
cost of cattle for stocking extra breeders is necessary to absorb
some of the irrigated feed crop. Wheat is shown as an independent

[1]Other investments are lower; they require no effort,
labor, or risk from the investor. A situation similar to savings
and loan company investment or government bonds is assumed.

[2]Grassland considers the stocking with range cattle;
therefore, the initial three or four years would yield little profit. The figure quoted is prorated for a ten-year period, although at any time during the first ten years much of the investment could have been liquidated with probable loss. After ten
years the herd furnishes its own breeder stock and the profits increase exponentially to surpass the other investments.

81

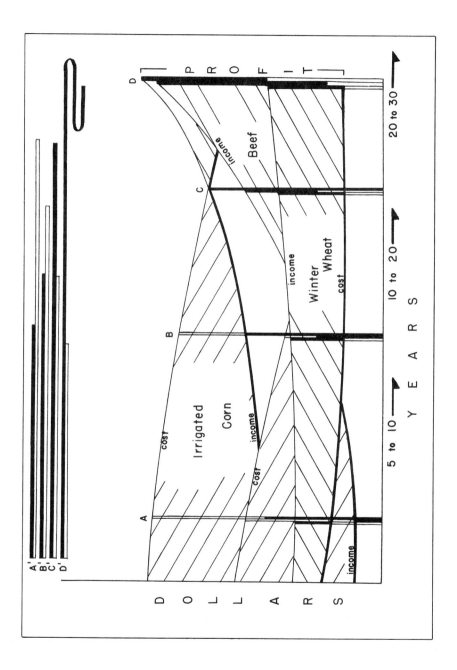

Figure 14

of the other methods and would expand or contract only slightly depending on changes in acreage. This graph depicts the alternatives that present irrigators have faced and what potential irrigators should contemplate. The indications are that:

1. For long-term benefit and stability, the integration of the three processes offers the greatest potential for income with least long-term risk.

2. For short-term, low investment, winter wheat offers security--even with hazards. But present-future income potential is low with specialization in winter wheat. In ten to twenty years profits from irrigation and cattle increase exponentially-- wheat profits increase slowly.

3. Irrigation, alone, offers high net profits only after several years of operation.

Attainments and Expectations

Irrigation has attained acceptance in the Colorado Northern High Plains. There are still skeptics who say, "Irrigation is only a hobby for the speculative farmer," yet economically, irrigation seems to have greater long-range stability than dryland farming. Late in the 1950's a local newspaper editor commented that irrigation can save the family farm in the High Plains. Recently there has been considerable interest by local Rotary Clubs, town councils, farmer groups, etc. in the possibility of mining the ground water supply by too much irrigation. Investigation shows that none of these extreme views is sound. Even though irrigation is expanding, farm sizes are growing and the population continues to decrease. There is no incentive for the small farmer to irrigate as he must have an assured net income every year. Consequently, irrigation accelerates the consolidation of farms, as diversity is necessary to establish a stable productive farm system. Irrigation will deplete the ground water eventually, but at the present development rate this seems unlikely for the next 30 to 50 years. Expansive farms which cover several square miles actually conserve the water supply as wells are more distributed. A study by the author in 1961 showed that one well per 2,300 acres (approximately four square miles) would probably never seriously damage the water quantity.[1]

Individual Case Histories

An example of what 10 years of irrigation has meant to one farm enterprise points up aspects of the situation in general. With many of the farm-irrigators in the High Plains there is neither great enthusiasm or blank rejection of the irrigation process. The following case illustrates both the positive gains that can be made by irrigating as well as some of the pitfalls that can be anticipated:

> A farmer in Yuma County made a decision to integrate irrigation, cattle feeding, and dryland farming in the 1950's based on the following line of thinking. He had two pre-teenage sons and was very much aware of the trend of young people away from the farm. He felt his dryland operation and cattle grazing program was sufficient for economic stability for himself and one son, but that it could not adequately support three families. He reasoned that if he could not practically afford to establish both sons in farmsteads, he might

---

[1] Bowden, op. cit.

<u>improve</u> his enterprise to include income potential
for a father-sons operation. He installed an
irrigation well in 1954. The sons reacted favorably to the idea and irrigation deemed the solution to finding a local outlet for his sons' am-
bitions. His cattle herd expanded from 40 to
almost 400, and he also concentrated on irrigated
feed crops plus two sections of dryland wheat and
sorghum. Today he has a profitable operation that
furnishes work and income for himself and both
sons.

His well laid plans did not find fruition,
however. Both sons attended college, and the elder
decided to leave the farm. What effect did this
have? The farmer, now middleaged, is operating
an enterprise (with one son) at an age when he
would like to retire. One son cannot handle the
irrigation, dryland farming, and cattle feeding
alone. Hired laborers are difficult to secure,
because the young man who used to look for summer
farm work has moved to the city with its ease,
security and excitement.

How does the farm father feel about his situation? He says, "I could have attained the same
results without the well, turned the dryland farm
over to my younger son, and retired years earlier.
Now the well and the pressure of cattle feeding
have become a burden. True, I've made more money,
but the labor, tension, and confinement that go
with irrigation are much greater than I expected.
Now I must face selling part of the land, watch
my son over work, or do the same myself."

In interviews with twenty-two of the irrigators in an

area of northwest Yuma County, twelve admitted that their work

load had increased more than they had anticipated. They believed

it required twice as much work to irrigate one quarter section as

to dryland farm an entire section of wheat. Although in every

case this sample group said their work per yield of crops had

decreased. Discussion with county agents and soil conservation

district agents through the area confirmed this as typical of the

region. This increased work load detracts from the appeal of irrigation considering the ages of the farmers in this region. (Less than one-fourth are under 45.) Throughout the area, irrigator and non-irrigator volunteered, "That irrigation is a good idea for the young."

Social Changes from Irrigation

Social acceptance of irrigation and the irrigator is unquestioned. In many instances the well(s) and land were acquired or owned by a father and operated by his son(s). There are no outsiders who have moved in to participate in irrigation. Consequently, all irrigators were either established farmers or at least members of the same community in which they installed a well. And wells were generally established on family- or personally-owned property. Therefore, there has been no change in land tenure, no immigration of work force, and no changes in the ethnic structure because of irrigation.

In other areas irrigation cliques were formed in the early stages,[1] but there is no evidence of a new irrigators' club in the study area. When thirty irrigators were asked, "How many friends do you have who irrigate?" 25 per cent said more than fifty, 30 per cent said more than twenty five, and 40 per cent said more than ten. Non-irrigators gave almost identical responses. The only significant difference was that 90 per cent of the irrigators knew other irrigators beyond their neighborhood. This

---

[1] E. M. Rogers and R. L. Pitzer, "The Adoption of Irrigation by Ohio Farmers," (Wooster, Ohio Agricultural Experiment Station) Research Bulletin 851, June, 1960 found evidence of an irrigators' club among innovators, especially at the early stages of development.

would not be true of non-irrigators who do not attend county or state meetings of special interest to irrigators.

Personal Opinions

Thirty five non-irrigator neighbors were asked, "Which best describes how you feel about irrigation?" Thirty per cent were interested; 20 per cent felt it was a good idea but needed to be proven; but 45 per cent believed it was not for them. Almost half considered irrigation a good idea, but too expensive.

A local banker views irrigation expansion as a gradual process that will come with large farm enterprises. He feels that most land will continue in dryland crops and irrigation will support livestock as a source of feed crops. The banker is understandably hesitant to finance wells for older farmers or small, indebted operators. Yet, his personal opinion is that the family farm is the backbone of the region and is most beneficial to the merchant and service functions in the local towns. Without the family farm there are few consumers; with the family farm there is a danger of depressed regional income and individual hardship.

Because this banker may grant loans for well installations, he was asked if he thought there was a particular group or type of person who could be identified as an irrigator. He replied that from his experience there is a certain economic level that makes a farmer eligible for this type of loan--but requests come from a wide range of local applicants. This means that a wider income range wants irrigation than the income group that can receive approved bank backing. The banker named several farmers as ideally suited for a well installation loan who had not shown any interest in attaining one. He suspects that lack of contact or experience with the practice is the basis of disinterest.

In conversations with farmers throughout the area, a statement "I don't know anything about irrigation and I'm too old to learn," was often repeated. However, when individual farmers lived near irrigators they were often able to give meaningful observations about their neighbor's project. Perhaps they knew more about irrigation than they realized or cared to admit. When there was no well nearby, the statement was probably true.

Summary

Irrigation in the Colorado Northern High Plains is economically gainful if the farmer is willing to invest for the long term. There is a considerable increase in work load and operating costs. Despite the conservation of older farmers, irrigation has established a foothold in the region.

There has been success but not without sacrifice. As a result the continuation of irrigation development and its innovation by more farmers encounters mixed emotions. There is a desire and need to change resource use to make greater profits on one hand and hesitancy to break away from traditional practices and accept new responsibility on the other.

There seems to be regional agreement that irrigation is good for the young farmer, but few young farmers live in the area. Nevertheless irrigation continues to expand at a consistent rate year after year. Potential adopters are evenly divided in their opinions as to whether they will or will not adopt; while the group in favor is again divided as to timing--to do it now or wait a few years. Individual opinions seem as varied as the number of installations.

An expansion or conversion to pump irrigation is definitely influenced by the way an innovator sees the benefit to himself. He assesses that benefit by what contacts he has with existing irrigation projects or with people who discuss irrigation. The communication of ideas and how they may influence the future development of irrigation is of considerable importance.

CHAPTER IV

SIMULATION OF DIFFUSION OF IRRIGATION WELLS IN THE
COLORADO NORTHERN HIGH PLAINS

The spatial pattern of irrigation well locations appears at
first glance to be haphazard or random. It can be shown that wells
exist in one locality for reasons which differ from those giving
rise to well installation in other locations.[1] Each irrigator has
a specific explanation for this decision to adopt irrigation and
different personal motives for innovating the change in resource
use do exist.[2] These personal motives do not mean that individuals
install wells for reasons chosen at random, but rather that the
multiplicity of reasons causes a spread of wells which appears in
total to be random in time and space. On the Colorado Northern

---

[1]One example of this is the natural gas situation. Because
natural gas furnishes low cost fuel and reduces operating expenses,
it would appear as an important conducive element in locating concentrations of wells. An attempt to correlate new well installations with distribution of natural gas showed that some areas had
irrigation units that followed natural gas lines, some areas had
natural gas lines but not irrigation wells, (other factors being
equal), and many areas had irrigation concentrations without natural gas. In other words, the availability of natural gas is help-
ful, but it is not a prime motivator nor does its absence necessar-
ily curtail installation of pump irrigation.

[2]It is understood that any resource manager involved in private enterprise makes a decision to change primarily to improve
his income--for the short or long term. Here, interest is in why
the decision was made to change to pump irrigation--not merely that
a change was performed.

High Plains wells appear to spread in all directions (Figure 15),
even though they are generally confined to the potential irrigable
areas delimited in Chapter II. Within this spread there are core
clusters. New well installations seem to decrease in number as
one moves farther away from earlier wells. Thus, the nearer a
neighbor is to a pump installation the greater are the chances he
will hear about or observe an operating well and adopt irrigation.
Hägerstrand states that,

> It is self evident that nobody can adopt an inno-
> vation without first having gained knowledge about
> its existence (except the inventor).
>
> The talking and listening individual is part
> of a huge, world-embracing network of links. A
> good many observations suggest that this network
> has a definite spatial structure which probably
> is rather stable, that is the links connect dif-
> ferent places with probabilities which presumably
> change only slowly and thus to some extent are
> predictable . . . .
>
> From daily experience we know that the links
> in the network of private communications must
> differ in spatial range between different socio-
> economic groups. As a demonstration and entirely
> arbitrarily we can make three groups operating in
>   international
>   regional and
>   local range.
> Some individuals are wholly bound to the local
> plane, and still others more or less on all
> three planes.[1]

The Colorado Northern High Plains represents a regional plane,
while within this framework are numerous local planes. The farmer
must be considered wholly bound to the local and regional planes
and not accessible to the international plane because of his

---

[1] Torsten Hägerstrand, "On Monte Carlo Simulation of Diffusion," (University of Lund, Sweden: 1953), pp. 4 and 5.

91

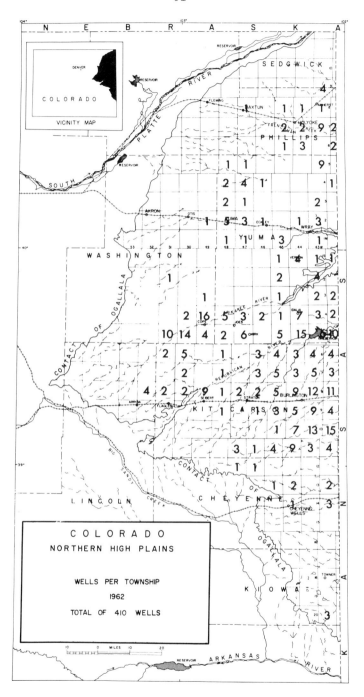

Figure 15

occupation and geographic location. The Colorado Northern High Plains includes similar socio-economic groups within which there may exist a network whereby ideas are communicated. An attempt is made here to establish that there is such a communication network on both local and regional planes, and that this network influences the adoption of pump irrigation.

Communicating Ideas about Irrigation

The adoption of pump irrigation by a neighbor affects the decision of a potential irrigator. Consequently, a resource manager who engages in discussions about a neighbor's well is influenced by what he sees and hears. This does not imply that he will immediately install a well or reject innovation, but he will certainly be more aware of irrigation than will a potential innovator who lives several miles from a pumping well.

The following is an example of communication on the local plane. Figure 16 shows the location of 23 wells installed during a ten-year period (1951-1960) in western Yuma County. Within this area there are two clusters of wells--one concentrated around the town of Yuma and a widely dispersed pattern in the north-central part. Two or three wells seem isolated or do not belong to a group. If a social network exists, a new well would likely be installed on a farmstead adjoining a farm with a well, etc. Assume that for this particular locale, all wells installed are installed within two farm sites of a previous well. The average size of farms in western Yuma County is two square miles; therefore, no well should be farther than two farm sites or four miles from other wells. Figure 16 shows that several wells are more than

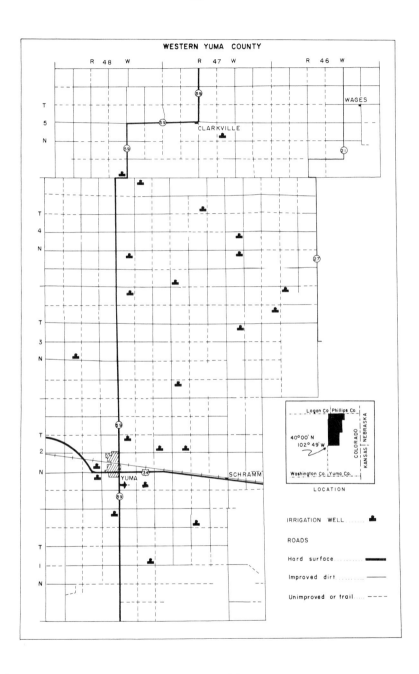

Figure 16

four miles from a previous well. However, as shown in Figure 17, none of the farm sites that have wells is farther than two farm sites or four miles from farm sites with existing wells. In this era of modern farm machinery, good roads, and fast transportation, farm land is no longer concentrated around one central location and may be widely dispersed. Because the farmer traverses all his land innumerable times during a year, irrigators and potential irrigators can observe one another or be in contact many times throughout the year. Consequently, a farmer cannot help but be influenced by what he sees or hears and he will be more aware of irrigation if he farms land near a producing well.

Social communication about irrigation on the local plane should influence a similar spread or diffusion of wells on a regional plane. The closer a potential irrigation site is to an existing irrigation area, the more likely it is to have new wells. Over a period of years adjacent areas should show more adoptions than locales not in contact with operating wells. Figure 18 shows this concept of diffusion from a core. The figure was constructed to show areas that were not more than two farmsteads away from an existing well. In this case, two farmsteads is assumed to be an area of four miles radii plus one mile for the farm that contains the well. This figure also incorporates a time-lag to allow for installation, communication, etc. For example, the 1948 choropleth is made up of 1946 farms with wells plus two farmsteads distance in all directions. (When the measurement fell into an area of non-potential irrigation, it was not depicted.) A sequence of maps showing yearly installations--1948 through 1963--was compared

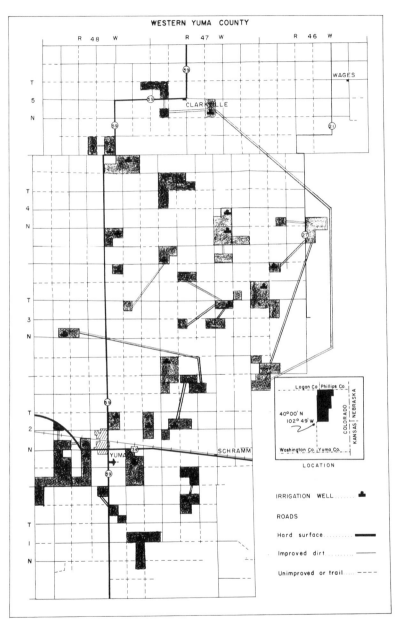

Figure 17. Shaded areas are lands held by the irrigator during
some period between 1951-60 (not just irrigated land).

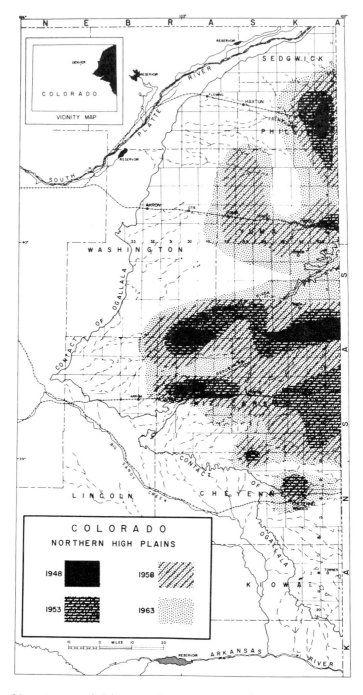

Figure 18.   Areas within two farmsteads of irrigation plots.

with the areas defined in Figure 18. In almost every case, new
installations occurred within the area defined as "no more than
two farmsteads out from existing wells."

This is parallel to Hägerstrand's approach to the Monte
Carlo simulation of diffusion of certain rural phenomena in Sweden.
He assessed that each existing phenomenon was a _teller_ of its idea
and that the ideas spread with the probabilities of contact being
higher the nearer to a teller the potential _receiver_ was located.[1]
Thus Hägerstrand suggested that in the nebula-like distribution
from clusters there seemed to be a "diffusion of techniques and
ideas through the network of social contact."[2] He proposed that,

> The spatial order in the adoption of innovations
> is very often so striking that it is tempting to
> try to create theoretical models which simulate
> the process and eventually make certain predic-
> tions achievable.[3]

To create a model that will simulate the process and make certain
predictions or projections requires development of a "mean information field" (MIF).[4] The purpose of this model is to project future
well development through simulating the location and number of

---

[1] Torsten Hägerstrand, _Innovationsforloppet ur korologisk synpunkt_, (The Innovation Process from a Chorological Point of View), Meddelanden fran Lunds Universitets Geografiska Institution, Avhandlingar XXV, Lund: Glearupska University Bokhandeln, 1953).

[2] Hägerstrand, "On Monte Carlo Simulation of Diffusion," _op. cit._, p. 1. The _receiver_ is the recipient of an idea and the _teller_ the carrier of information.

[3] _Ibid._, p. 4.

[4] MIF is an identifiable pattern of communication. It refers to the probability of communication per unit of distance outward from a teller or broadcaster. Information declines in impact and hence the MIF is a uni-modal field declining outward with increasing distance from a teller.

present wells from information as to original innovations and the
probabilities of social interaction described by the MIF, and then
to project the diffusion of new wells into the future. This type
of simulation is useful in determining the quantity and location of
future water resource use, estimating the potential depletion of
the ground water supply, and projecting the physical, economic, and
legal aspects that may be anticipated. The procedure used to build
the model requires several progressive steps: (1) to determine the
limits within which the projection can operate, (2) to measure
some known pattern of communication over space that can be used to
simulate irrigation adoption, (3) to construct from this pattern
of communication a probability model to serve as a MIF, (4) to
test the model by simulating the past diffusion of wells and comparing the results with actual patterns of well installations,
(5) to apply the model to a projection of the future diffusion of
wells, and finally (6) to evaluate the future projections as they
apply to the physical, socio-economic and legal situation of the
future.

Limits within which the Projection can Operate

Some basic assumptions about the area are necessary before
proceeding. These constitute the limits of the model and projections.

1. The region will continue to depend upon agriculture
   as an economic base.

2. There will be no radical fluctuations in government
   policy (on all levels) or consumer attitudes of the
   buying public.

3. Prices received for farm products will remain relatively constant in relation to each other.

4. Technological developments will increase but at a steady rate.

Measurement of Communication which can be Simulated

Various media of communication were investigated to find those which could be related to the idea of irrigation adoption. In line with Hägerstrand, a local area relation was discovered through the attendance at a free barbecue in one of the towns. Here the communication pattern is represented by travel. At this event, the head of household or his wife registered for a raffle while waiting to receive the meal. From this registration, data were plotted by home location on a land occupancy map furnished by the area Commodity Credit Corporation. This information was checked by cross-reference with land ownership data furnished by the county treasurer's office, which gave occupancy in land ownership. Registration at the barbecue is shown on the following table.

TABLE IX
REGISTRATION AT FREE BARBECUE
(in Yuma)

Number in attendance	Distance traveled (miles)	Percentage
493	0 - 1.0	47.1
216	1.1 - 5.0	20.6
191	5.1 -10.0	18.2
57	10.1 -15.0	5.4
38	15.1 -20.0	3.6
17	20.1 -25.0	1.6
29	25.1 -30.0	2.8[1]
4	30.1 -35.0	.5
2	35.1 -40.0	.2
Total 1047		100.0

[1]The break in linear decrease at 25.1-30.0 miles in the table is probably the influence of Wray, a town of similar size to Yuma but with closer ties than other towns, i. e. county seat, etc.

At first it seemed unrealistic to include the town populace (those who traveled only one mile in the table) in a surrogate for the communication of a strictly rural innovation. However, most of the market towns throughout the region are (1) about the same size, (2) the centers of communication, (3) in contact with all rural people, and (4) contain a great many of the recent "sidewalk farmers" previously mentioned.

These data might be used to provide an MIF which in this area would be restricted to the local plane. In order to combine a local communication network with regional communication other data were sought.

Because of the uniform physical character of the Colorado High Plains, and although homogeneous in socio-economic respects, there is no easily defined internal communication pattern. Newspapers are local, not regional; transportation is well linked but is only a part of a greater network which centers in Denver. Interregional telephone calls seemed the best data to establish a regional communication pattern. (Marriage records, exchange of farm labor, farm organization membership and similar surrogates were not applicable.) There are eleven telephone exchanges in the region; each center handles a local area of from 25 to 45 mile radii and serves approximately the same number of subscribers. Because almost all equipment is automatic, there is no logging of local calls--only long distance. A typical list of such calls from Yuma in one month is shown in the following table.

TABLE X

LONG DISTANCE CALLS FROM YUMA, COLORADO IN A MONTH

Destination City	Percentage of calls
Otis (12 miles)	22.7[1]
Wray (26 miles)	40.0
Akron (27 miles)	18.8
Joes, Kirk, Cope (35 miles)	9.1
Haxtun (36 miles)	1.4
Holyoke (40 miles)	4.7
Seibert (56 miles)	.8
Burlington (60 miles)	.6
Julesburg (65 miles)	.8
Cheyenne Wells (92 miles)	1.1
Kit Carson (95 miles)	0
	100.0

A combination of long distance telephone calls and barbecue attendance data from one center satisfies both regional and local aspects of communication. The calls have a complementary effect in that the greatest number of calls are at the farther distances (beyond 25 miles), while the greatest number in attendance at a free meal were nearer in distance to the center.

With these data, it was possible to build a diffusion model of communication on a regional basis. The frequencies of contact were plotted against the logarithm of the distance out from a center. Then, by calculating a least squares line, Figure 19, the expected probability of a _receiver_ hearing an idea at a specific distance from a _teller_ could be measured.

Application of a Monte Carlo grid to Idea Communication

The probability of installation of an irrigation well is

---

[1]Although Otis is just 12 miles from Yuma, the relative low percentage is understandable. Most of the population utilizes Yuma (about four times larger) as a market center and more direct communication is available without long distance calls. The percentage on barbecue attendance offset this figure.

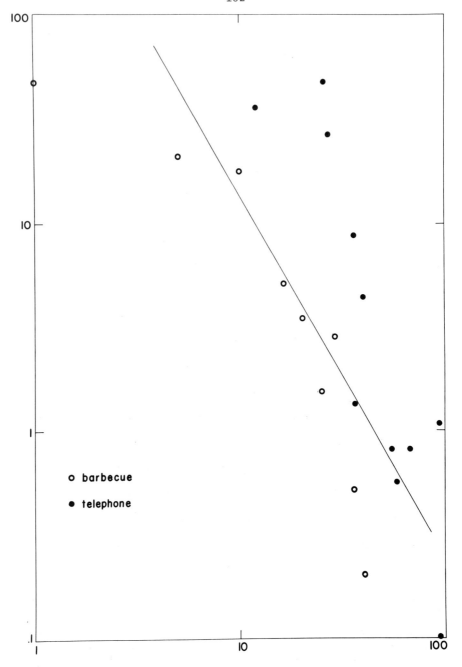

Figure 19. Out-migration of percentage of long distance telephone
calls and attendance at barbecue from Yuma. Horizon-
tal axis is in miles and vertical axis is per cent of
frequency of occurrence.

higher the nearer an individual lives to an existing well. The

pattern of contacts is assumed to be uniform with respect to di-

rection. Individual occurrences are random. The expected pattern

of contacts verses distance is shown in Table XI which is extra-

polated from Figure 19.

TABLE XI

Distance from teller	Range of interaction	Probability of contact
1 to 5 miles	1.000 to .420	.580 (58 out of 100)
5.1 to 10 miles	.419 to .130	.290 (29 out of 100)
10.1 to 20 miles	.129 to .040	.090 (9 out of 100)
20.1 to 30 miles	.039 to .020	.020
30.1 to 40 miles	.019 to .012	.008 (4 out of 100)
beyond 40 miles	.011 to .000	.012
		1.000

In order to simulate the random character, a model was construc-

ted on an azimuthal grid[1] using the calculated probability of

teller-receiver contact. The model is designed to give equal

chance of contact or hearing about an irrigation installation at

any point equi-distant from the teller. The teller is assumed to

be located in the center of the grid (Figure 20). The probability

of a new well being installed by a farmer decreases with distance

from an earlier well because the farmer does not receive the

---

[1]An azimuthal grid was chosen rather than a square grid
pattern because of ease of application. The inter-regional communication is assumed to be omni-directional. This method differs
somewhat from Hägerstrand's 5 x 5 km grid in that as one goes out
from the center the sectors become larger in area. The azimuthal
grid used for the runs was divided into 25 sectors so that up to
40 miles, the local plane taken from the barbecue, was incorpora-
ted and no sector was larger than the average size of a farmstead.
Beyond 40 miles the location was determined by the location of the
random probability within the sector. Each concentric ring was
also added by average farm size. In earlier experimental stages
both systems were attempted and results were comparable.

104

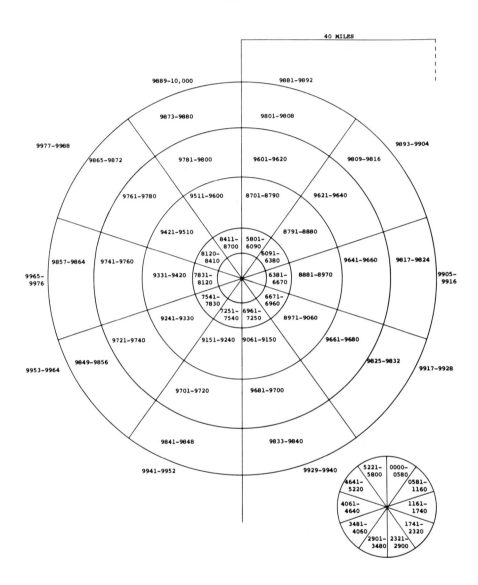

Figure 20.   Simplified example of Azimuthal Grid used to generate
diffusion process. Each radius arc is equal to 10
miles with the exception of the inner two, which are 5
miles. On the actual grid used, the probabilities were
divided into 1 mile radii up to 12 miles (2 times the
side of a township) and 5 mile radii after that. Instead of ten sectors as shown here, the work grid con-
sisted of 25 sectors.

"message" as often. The random element is produced by assuming that all azimuthal directions have equal chance of receiving. Therefore, by taking azimuthal direction and predetermined probabilities as they appear on Figure 20, the area of probable installation of a new well can be located using a random number table. For example, the probability of a new well being drilled within 5 miles of a previous well is .58 or about 6 chances out of ten. The numbers from 0000 to 5800 are divided into equal sectors as shown by the insert in Figure 20. A four-digit random number of 1746 would fall in the right hand side of the fourth clock-wize sector which is sector 1741 through 2320.

Before a simulated diffusion run can be performed there are certain rules which must govern the model. The following are modifications of Hägerstrand's rules and are adapted to fit the problem of the spread of irrigation wells in the Colorado High Plains.

1. One well installation generates the idea at the start.

2. One well installation influences only one other potential well installation in each generation of the model.

3. The probability of communication depends on the distance between teller and receiver.

4. There are several generations of telling, with each new generation having been told on a pair-wise basis by wells from the previous generation.

5. The uniform farm density results in an even distribution of potential innovators in areas where irrigation is possible.[1]

-----

[1]There is an assumed limit of one well per farm and potential innovators live only on farms capable of irrigation which do not already have a well.

This fifth rule necessitated some modifications to a <u>regional</u> communication of innovation. In earlier chapters it was established that within the region there are only specific areas that have ground water potential for irrigation development. This boundary, therefore, impedes irrigation development. Consequently, except when a contact occurs in the marginal fringe, any teller-receiver contact that falls outside Class I and Class II land with less than 500 gpm potential is rejected. (Refer to discussion and figures in Chapter II.) When this happens the simulation run moves on to the next teller. No new well is installed when an existing well tells a farm that already has a well, or tells only within the same farm site as it exists, or tells a receiver that lies outside the irrigable area.

> 6. Any township that contains more than 16 wells is considered saturated and removed from the simulation run.

This rule is based on information from Chapter III and is obviously subjective. However, this judgment is made because: (1) no present (1962) township has more than 16 wells and all townships that approach 16 drop rapidly in new well installation, (2) natural recharge of ground water will not sustain more than 16 wells per township except in dune sand which is a reject area, (3) land tenure occupance averages about 16 farmers per township, (4) county- or area-wide saturation of 16 or more wells per township would probably encourage legislation to curtail installation and pumping or judicial action by non-irrigators who depend on ground water for stock and domestic supply.

A simulation model was constructed using 410 random hits

to represent the 410 actual wells which existed in 1962. The azimuthal grid was applied in the following manner.

1. Using a map of operation well locations in 1948
    (Figure 21) the center of the azimuthal grid was
    placed on a well; next a selection was made from
    a table of four-digit random numbers. Locating that
    chosen number on the grid gave the simulated location
    of a receiver of the idea from the teller well.[1]

2. Each established well told a new well the following
    year, but if the receiver was not eligible as defined
    in rules 5 and 6, then the grid was moved to a new
    teller and a new random number was selected.

3. If the random location occurred within a mile of a
    teller well or another well, the grid was moved on.

4. The simulation was continued until the saturation
    point of 16 wells per township was reached.

The initial point of each run was chosen at random by

selecting the township and range numbers from a random number

table. By reading the table vertically until a township number

with wells present was located and doing the same horizontally

for range numbers the starting point was located. Figure 22 shows

the resultant locations by township of the 410 simulated wells

as compared with the actual 1962 location in Figure 15. Figure 23

represents a continuation of pair-wise runs into the future. The

various townships become saturated at 16 wells in the years indi-

cated. The generation considered here is simply a continuous pair-

wise run until townships drop out because of saturation. By 1990,

681 wells should theoretically be dropped as tellers. The town-

ships with 14 or 15 wells are symbolized and would saturate in a

---

[1]All runs were performed at a scale of 1/250,000 on AMS
maps of the region.

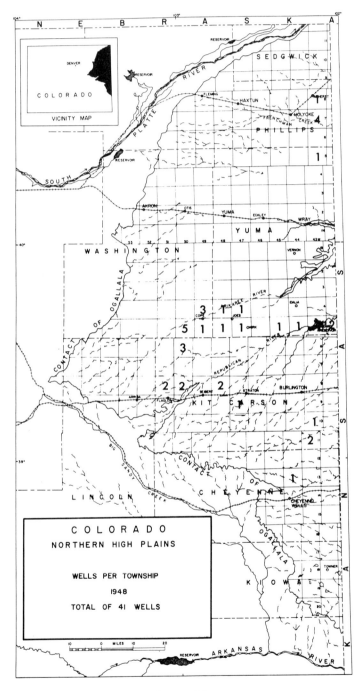

Figure 21

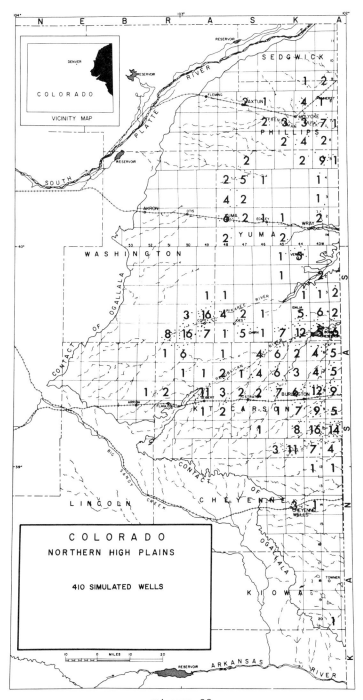

Figure 22

110

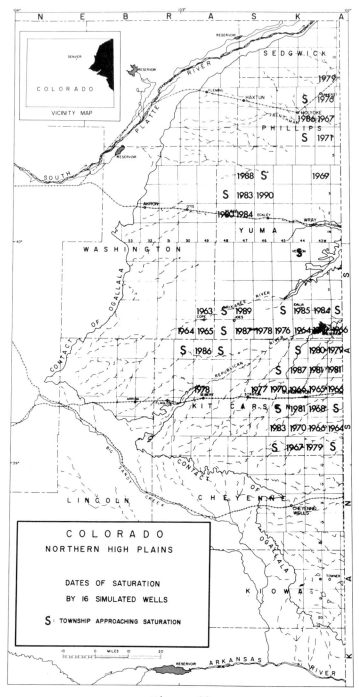

Figure 23

few more runs. This is to be expected because the rules allow a rate of diminishing installation the nearer a township gets to the saturation point. For example, it is very difficult to get a pair-wise hit in a township of 15 wells because most of the hits fall on land with previous wells or in non-irrigable land.

Ten simulation runs were performed up to 1962 to compare with the 1962 actual location map (Figure 15) and to provide estimates of the expected diffusion pattern and the variance possible. The generation was determined by one well telling a new well and repeating the procedure each year. Under the pair-wise rule each well should tell another well the following year. However, as in the case of Figure 22 once a new well is told it may be located two to three miles distant; this increases the rejection area that the teller and receiver present the third year. Although one well tells another, a cluster of five or six wells may only tell one or two new wells because of the overlap of the MIF.

The simulations illustrated consistent similarity to the actual well locations. In total, the accumulative figures for simulated runs were: (1) 438, (2) 418, (3) 371, (4) 395, (5) 405, (6) 431, (7) 399, (8) 369, (9) 421, (10) 415. Results of the run with total wells (405) nearest both the mean of sumation of all runs (406.1) and to the actual number of wells (410) are shown in Figure 24. Figure 25 represents the mean number of simulated wells per township of all ten runs. Because some townships do not receive a well on certain simulation attempts, the mean is at times a fraction and is therefore rounded off to the nearest whole number. Figure 25 shows a total of 408 wells because of the "rounding

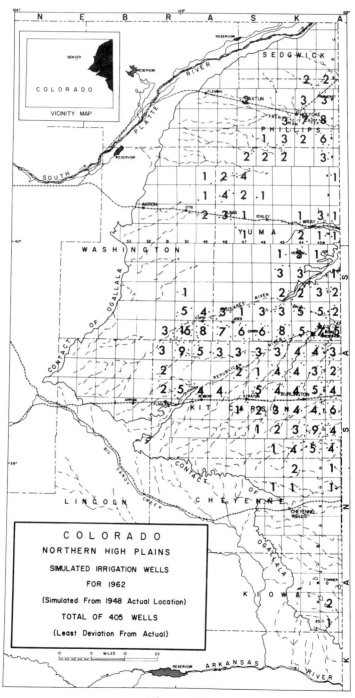

Figure 24

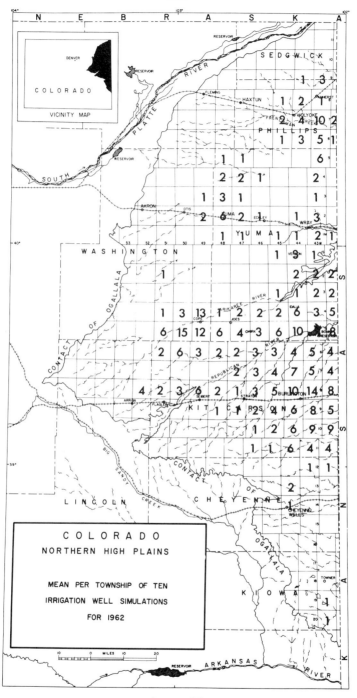

Figure 25

off" of numbers in certain townships.

By comparing the actual number of wells per township from Figure 15 with the mean of ten simulations per township in Figure 25, variance and similarity in distribution can be observed from Table XII.

Wells per township	1	2	3	4	5	6	7	8	9	10	11	12	13	14	15	16
Actual		34	22	13	12	8	2	2	0	5	2	1	1	1	1	1	1
Simulated		37	26	14	10	6	9	2	3	2	3	0	1	1	1	1	0

TABLE XII

Projecting Future Diffusion of Wells

Future simulation of the diffusion of wells is accomplished by the same approach that was used to replicate the development of the present pattern of locations.[1] Figures 26 and 27 are the result of simulated projection for future spread of pump wells in the Colorado High Plains for 1975 and 1990. By this method, it can be projected that there will be 901 wells in the region by 1975 and 1644 wells by 1990, considering 681 wells have been dropped as tellers. According to the rules established earlier, a saturation point of 16 wells per township was the cutoff whose effect is shown by a saturation symbol. Figure 28 is a continuous simulation projection without saturation and shows the probable diffusion of wells if 16 is not a proper upper limit for

[1]Due to the fluctuating number of well installations per year, a logistic growth curve was plotted to determine an average upper limit for the number of wells installed in one year. The maximum number extrapolated from the curve was assumed the highest value for any useable random number.

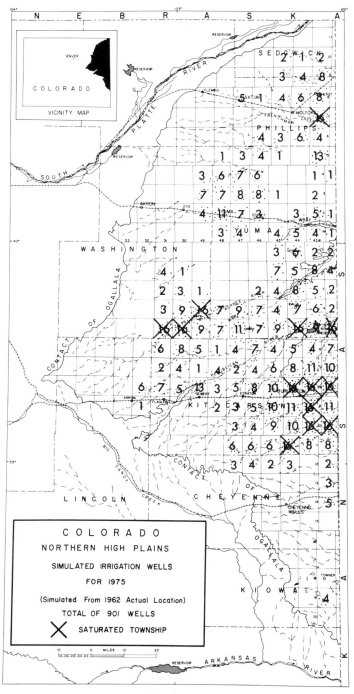

Figure 26

116

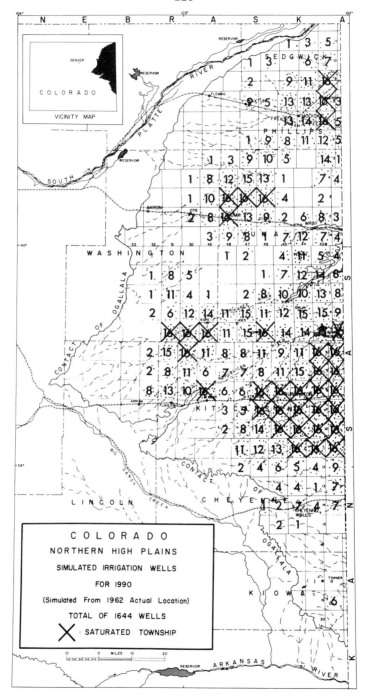

Figure 27

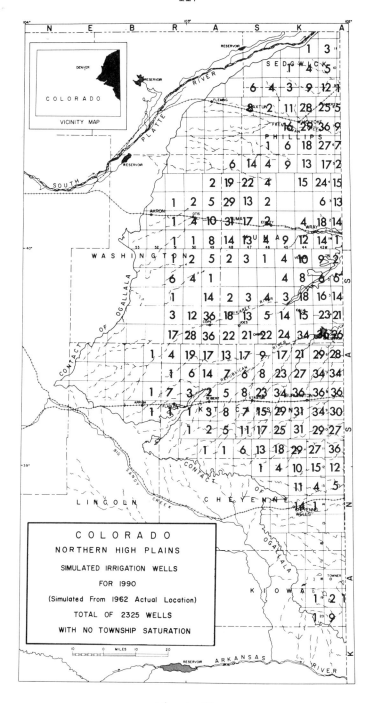

Figure 28

a specific township.[1]

One of the original purposes of making an estimate of future well numbers was to ascertain the rate of depletion of the ground water resources. Figures 29 and 30 portray (1) the accumulative growth of wells with saturation of 16 wells per township and without saturation, (2) the accumulative non-recoverable depletion of ground water (assuming the saturation curve is real) and the decrease in stored, recoverable and non-recoverable ground water under irrigable land in the entire region. Also a curve is shown of the decrease in total ground water. Utilizing well production data and length of pumping season determined in Chapters II and III, the accumulative ground water withdrawal should approach 20 million acre-feet by 1990.[2] This does not consider the effect of ground water control by law.

<u>Summary</u>

Individual farmers in the Colorado Northern High Plains have specific reasons for adopting or avoiding pump irrigation, and in general diffusion of wells depends on the probability of contact with an established well and declines with distance. From a group of core wells unit density decreased with distance but appears to diffuse through space in random direction.

---

[1]However, no township is allowed more than 36 or one well per square mile because of the model rules.

[2]Domestic and stock demands on the water supply are assumed to be offset by natural recharge from precipitation. Therefore, both factors are constants and do not affect the curve. Even with increased feeder stock, the demand would remain in balance due to declining human consumption as the population decreases.

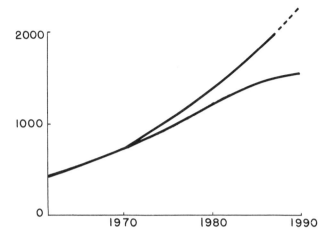

Figure 29. Projected total irrigation wells through 1990. Lower
curve simulates curve with 16 wells per township
saturation while upper curve is without saturation
factor.

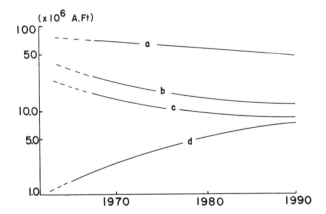

Figure 30. Accumulative depletion of ground water by irrigation
wells based on simulation models. a-total storage in
entire region, b-total recoverable in entire region,
c-total recoverable in irrigable land, and d-accumula-
tive use by irrigation wells.

A modification of Hägerstrand's Monte Carlo simulation of diffusion technique is used to create a receiver-teller model based on communication by long distance telephone calls and attendance at a barbecue. Those data provided a mean information field which was translated into an azimuthal grid that described the most probable communication patterns over distance. Simulated patterns compare very favorably with actual patterns. Using this same technique projections of future wells and the expected withdrawal of ground water are offered. The validity of projection of expansion and development is speculative. But this method offers an approach worthy of consideration by planners and managers in studying the effects of a change in resource use.

CHAPTER V

ASSESSMENT OF SEQUENT DEVELOPMENTS

Since 1962, when the field work for this study was completed, five occurrences have influenced the irrigation scene.
Although recent evidence is not conclusive enough to permit generalization, it is sufficient to speculate regarding new trends
in resource management practices in the Colorado Northern High
Plains.

1.   There has been severe drought throughout much of the
Colorado Northern High Plains during 1962-63-64. Except for small
enclaves of "normal" precipitation, the area has been receiving
about 5 inches less per year than the long term 17 inches average.

2.   Decline in beef cattle prices, along with loss of
feed crops by drought, has hampered the traditional economic buffer the High Plains farmers uses to bolster income when field
crops fail.

3.   Attempts to use irrigated sugar beets to increase income has attained erratic success. Control of sugar beets by
government acreage allotments creates a fluctuating situation in
which the whims of government decision and the resultant contracting by sugar companies produce varied legitimate sugar beet

121

acreage. In general, this variation has made sugar beets an unstable cropping practice.

4. Surplus stored commodities are depleted. Unsold or
stored grains and feed crops that clogged the hundreds of elevators and granaries throughout the region in the 1950's are gone.
Bins and storage areas are empty and local purchase feeder crops
are scarce and expensive. Crop failure from drought forced the
farmer and grain merchant to sell off surpluses; and for the first
time in decades, there is no local excess of wheat and other
grains within the area.

5. A final influence is the accumulative effect of the
first four. There is a regional feeling of apprehension about
the future. Except during the desperate years of the 1930's,
there has not been such a widespread fear of impending failure.
Low profit margins, debts, and continued crop failure have produced a pervading attitude that exploitation of any resource is
permissible to recover from, what is probably, the periodic and
re-occurring economic slump that plagues agriculturalists in all
of the world's semi-arid steppe lands.[1] There is evidence that

----

[1]Perception of drought, attitude toward hazards, and
changing outlook caused by minor economic fluctuations are little
understood but important aspects of the living environment in the
High Plains. The cliché of "a good year is normal, a normal year
is marginal, a substandard year is a disaster in the mind of the
farmer" fits well. Concepts of a dry year, insect invasion, hail
storms, disease or similar hazards vary greatly with yearly individual prosperity. For example, farmers who survived the 1930
dust bowl and depression will discuss it in terms of the great
disaster if confronted during a wet, productive year. In 1965,
after a short drought, the same farmer is willing to declare,
"things were never this bad in the '30's." Any investigator, who
interviews farmers in this region must constantly be aware that
"he will probably be told how bad things are" and rarely be

pump irrigation is the resource use that will be exploited.

Short Term Problems With Long Range Influences

Pump irrigation has become a pallative for recovery of economic stability in the Colorado Northern High Plains. In early 1965, there are 803 irrigation wells, 393 are new wells installed or contracted since 1962. (Figures 31 and 32)

Irrigation is widely discussed. The pros and cons of complementing an existing dryland system by adding a pump well dominate the conversation of farmers throughout the region. Irrigation equipment suppliers, well drillers, power suppliers, and other interested promoters are competitively bidding and attempting to entice the non-irrigator to drill a well. Consequently, some 47,000 acres of mostly Class I land have been converted to irrigation in the last three years (1965).

Divided Opinions

Casual criticism by non-irrigators and subdued irrigator enthusiasm prevailed for more than 15 years as the unproven practice gradually became part of the High Plains farming scene. This attitude no longer exists; opinions are deterministic and emphatic in defending or condemning the impact of irrigation. The contrast in scenes is dynamic; for example, Leslie Hewes in describing "A Traverse Across Kit Carson County..." devoted two lines to two

---

informed of "how good things are." It seems that years which are normal, in precipitation, crop yields, etc. are seldom recognized locally as being normal until several years later when the farmer recalls what happened back in 19--.

124

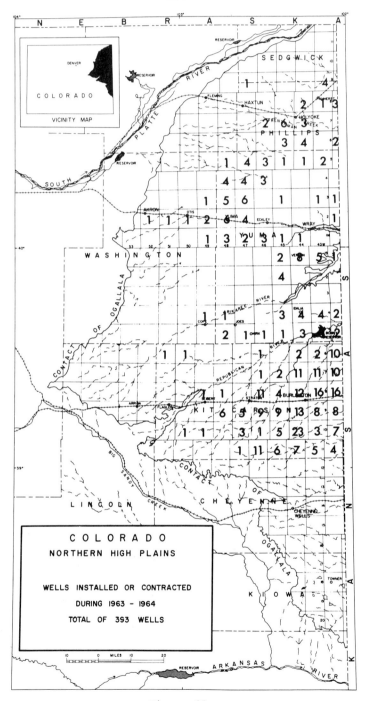

Figure 31

125

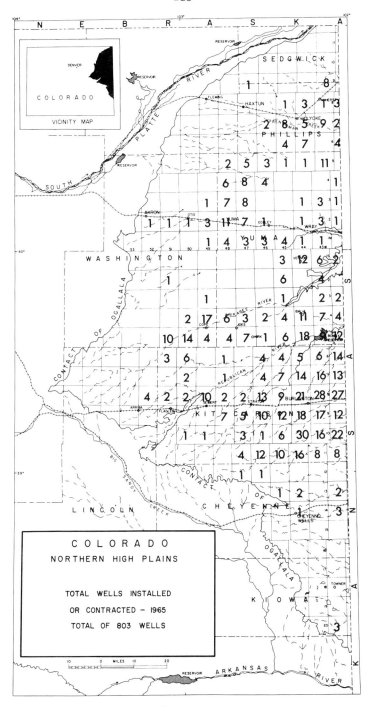

Figure 32

irrigated sorghum fields.[1] This same area now contains almost 100 operating pumps.

Although pumping of ground water has not reached a dangerous degree of water mining, more and more critics are aware that continuing irrigation development threatens the water supply. However, since calculations show that the present 803 wells would need more than 50 years to deplete the Ogallala water, the danger lies in exponential increase in the number of well units which would rapidly shorten this period. If the reasonable development assumed for the 1990 simulation model from Chapter IV remains valid (this situation is discussed later), there is enough ground water to supply irrigation increase for the remainder of the twentieth century.

Undermining an assumption of reasonable development, however, is an ominous threat to the future stability and prosperity of the Colorado Northern High Plains. This threat involves three observable changes of attitude toward resource management, some of which are obvious to local critics, some obscure, but significant. The changes are:

1. An increase in the number of two or more wells per one owner. About 15 per cent of the new installations are made by farmers owning a well. This occurrence is predictable because an irrigator, committed by one well to this type of land use, envisions the second well as a simple, less expensive expansion. The

---

[1]Leslie Hewes, "A Traverse Across Kit Carson County, Colorado, with notes on Land Use on the Margin of the Old Dust Bowl, 1939-40 and 1962," Economic Geography, Vol. 39, No. 4, October, 1963, pp. 332-340.

second installation is much cheaper and easier to maintain as the farmer has learned from experience and he has already tied up considerable capital in implements suited for irrigation. There are other influences, such as easy credit because the irrigator's image as "experienced, therefore potentially profitable" or "equipped and therefore more creditable" makes him a good financial risk. Most of these influences did not exist ten years ago. Therefore, the multi-well owner could be the innovator of a more complex resource management phase where irrigation comes to dominate the farm activities rather than supplement or complement the extensive dryland enterprise.

The multiple-well owner tends to locate his new well next to his irrigated land. There are immediate dollar gains to be realized from this practice--short haul of irrigation equipment, elimination of extensive power or fuel supply lines, water from the former well to cut costs of drilling the second well (usually water is hauled by tank truck during the mud-flow drilling phase), potential overlap of cropping systems and water distribution with more assurance of consistently available water, and a sense of security about obtaining a good yield if the earlier well was a high water yielder (which is usually the case). This close proximity of wells will shorten their useful life as cones of depression eventually coalesce and create a drop in the water table. Therefore, the present practice of two adjacent wells suggests a shorter period of irrigation than previously projected.

2. Middle age farmers are now investing in irrigation wells at a much faster rate. Early innovators were young farmers;

most under 45. Irrigation has continued to expand among established farmers and new installations are consequently by an older
group. A trend by older farmers to irrigate suggests a possible
unhealthy management situation eventually. Less than half of the
middle age farmers have heirs who will take over an enterprise as
operators. Although many farmers have large families, the age
differential is such that, by the time a farmer reaches 55 years,
his children have left the farm to establish themselves in urban
environments. Within the next 10 to 15 years, when the present
middle age farmer either retires or dies, his urban children will
inherit the land. Few of these urbanites will return to the farm
and the result will be an absentee ownership. Although the absentee
ownership problem faces all operations, it is particularly menacing
in terms of irrigation because absentee ownership is conducive to
exploited and mismanaged resource development. Lincoln and Kiowa
counties suffered the pangs of absentee land speculators, suitcase
farmers, and "get-rich-quick" schemers when they plowed and planted
marginal Class III land following World War II. The resultant
mismanagement created a heavily eroded surface that has not recovered. An analogous condition could be projected for irrigation,
with the Colorado Northern High Plains ground water supply the
victim.

      3. Irrigation has impressed enough financiers that both
local lenders and outside private or public agencies have relaxed
their rules on what it takes to get support for well installation.
In the initial stages of irrigation development, the innovator
often had to depend upon his dryland operation to furnish collateral

for irrigation loans, but in the mid-1960's required credit has eased and a large percentage can be financed, in some instances up to 90 per cent.

Borrowing money to irrigate is widespread and with lower restrictions people can begin to irrigate with less cash. Conversely, savings and cash available to individuals have been curtailed throughout the region because of recent dryland crop failures. A farmer going into irrigation can do so with less capital of his own and more financed than ever before. Unfortunately, some of the new operations are so marginal and so heavily in debt that one mishap or misjudgment, i.e., hailstorm, wrong fertilization, poor choice of seed, etc., and the irrigator could be bankrupt within a season.

Land values have not changed appreciably in the last ten years. So far, there is no rush to buy up irrigable land on the assumption that irrigation potential will inflate the price. The value of the installed well unit and equipment or machinery remains equal in value to the land it can irrigate. However, as irrigation expands, especially if there is no legislative control of water, irrigable land is destined to grow in price per acre.[1] Local realtors have received inquiries from interested investors

---

[1] There seems to be a complete lack of appreciation on the part of most farmers in this area that "once you commit a field to irrigation, you cannot expect to return to summerfallow wheat cropping at some future date if the water is no longer available." Primarily because irrigation is new and not fully established, the regional farmer doesn't understand the long term effects that artificial application of water to a zonal soil developed under semi-arid conditions will be. Soils that are irrigated change character, texture, mineral content, etc., even

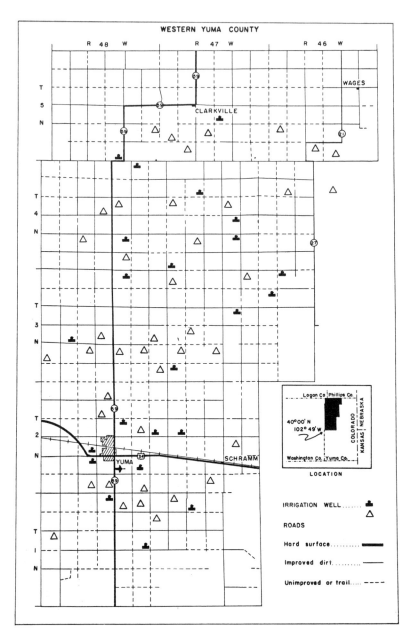

Figure 33. Triangles show location of irrigation wells drilled after 1960.

outside the region--men who are watching the irrigation development scene with intense interest.

The concept of buying land and developing it for irrigation with tenant or hired operators has been considered by several. There is one "irrigation well developer" in Kit Carson County who has been instrumental in having over 20 wells installed; however, these are mostly developed and then sold to another individual. Various enthusiasts in Phillips, Yuma, and Kit Carson Counties report having seriously considered either buying up adjoining land or using self-owned land to attempt an "irrigated farm corporation with tenant farmers." However, this approach was planned and initiated in Yuma County during 1959, but was abandoned due to high initial cost and lack of labor. Since the Yuma County venture is well known and considered a "failure" it tends to dampen the enthusiasm of several potential developers.

"To Control or Not to Control"--A Dilemma

The Northeastern Colorado Development Committee is a volunteer group of businessmen, county agents, political officials, etc., formed in 1963 to study economic trends and problems of the area. These men decided they would unite to coordinate ideas and

---

without intensive fertilization. The full understanding of what happens when you work with a new resource practice that involves a change in physical character from a previous practice is lacking in the Colorado Northern High Plains. It is quite true that the High Plains can be turned into an intensively water oasis similar to the surface water projects in many parts of the west. But once you have made this decision, there is little or no chance of turning back and the individual may well be destroying a base for practical development by some future generation, or creating a condition that makes it uneconomical to use the resource. The myth of the "Great American Desert" of the 19th century may become an actuality in the 21st century.

material that seemed beneficial for further economic development throughout the High Plains. Of the 15 or so regularly attending members, few were farmers--not that farmers were unwelcome, but seemed generally disinterested. Originally, the Committee was a three-county association, but later grew to include representatives from all the counties in the Colorado Northern High Plains.

Irrigation and ground water supply soon became the dominant concern of the Committee. Although other subjects were on the agenda, soon the entire Committee was persuaded to devote full time to collecting and studying available information in order to ascertain some direction about future benefits and dangers from increased irrigation. Within a relatively short time, the Committee was convinced that overdevelopment of ground water by irrigation could result in serious consequences for the future stability of the region.

The Committee also recognized that some water control was eventually to be forced--either within the region or from outside the region. There were indications that the city and county of Denver was considering the future tapping of the Ogallala for transportable water to its urban complexes. Planners in the Arkansas and South Platte River Basins had contemplated acquiring land and water rights in the Ogallala in order to pump ground water for transport to sugar beet allotted farm lands of the two water short basins. Naturally, the Committee wanted to keep the control of water within the Ogallala basin. Besides this conflict, there were individual uncertainties about restriction of irrigation as such curtailment meant the loss of business and possible immediate income for several Committee members. Despite personal conflicts, the Committee agreed action was necessary if the Colorado Northern High Plains was not to suffer overdevelopment, mining, and an eventual loss of water supply.

One of the stated concerns of the development committee was that water be controlled and regulated in an egalitarian manner for the greatest long term benefit. At the same time it desired the acquisition and maintenance of the right and use of ground water within the Ogallala basin. Therefore, an immediate goal was to encourage legislation by the state to declare the Ogallala a "closed basin"[1] with the water designated for the use and benefit of the people living in the basin.

In practice, the state of Colorado has no ground water law. About the only effect of the 1957 ruling (mentioned in the Forward of this book) was to require the registration of wells. Because of the ineffectiveness of the present law, the North-eastern Colorado Development Committee wanted a new law "with some teeth in it"--and they were not alone as several other closed basins within the state were pushing for new legislation. Although most members of the Colorado State Legislature believe there is need for an effective ground water law, many are not in favor of the closed basin concept. Some have proposed bills that assert all the ground waters of the State of Colorado should be declared

---

[1]Closed basin refers to an area that has internal source and supply of water and whose use of such does not interfere with beneficial use in other areas. Physically, the Ogallala is not a true closed basin because of underground flow to Nebraska and Kansas. The term "closed basin" is only legal jargon to define it in relation to the State of Colorado.

the property of the people of Colorado and used for whatever development is deemed best for the most people. In general, the confu-
sion and occasionally unweilding opinions create a legislative
stalemate. As this thesis goes to press, legislative action is
ensuing with good possibilities of passing a usable ground water
law. Regardless of whether the result is regional control or state
control, at least there is encouragement that long needed legal
regulation and method of control is about to be established.[1]

post tenebras lux

Today, approximately 20 per cent of the farmers living on
Class I and II land with more than 500 gpm ground water yield potential are involved in some form of irrigation. For example, in
the 400 square mile sample area of Western Yuma County there are
now 64 irrigation wells as contrasted to the 23 wells that existed
in 1960 (Figure 33). Some other local areas have experienced
greater saturation, i.e., Eastern Kit Carson County, while some
potentially favorable areas such as along Frenchman Creek in
Phillips County have lagged behind.[2] Because Western Yuma County

---

[1]There is another possible modification that can be anticipated unless whoever establishes the control anticipates this
adjustment, which is the installation of several small diameter
wells should regulation prohibit new installations of large diameter wells. In west Texas, there was control placed on the drilling
of large diameter irrigation wells and to circumvent the rule yet
continue to expand, the irrigator drills numerous small diameter
wells and continues expansion without restriction by legal control.

[2]One area of intense irrigation concentration is along
the Arikaree River in the Cope area of Southern Washington County.
This particular area is an anomaly to the general geologic pattern
of the Ogallala in that it is a combination of Recent alluvium and
older sands and gravels. At present there is an attempted artificial

represents the median in density pattern for Class I and II land

it is used as a comparison of actual well installation distribution

with simulated projections described in Chapter IV. A high posi-

tive correlation is apparent from Table XIII which lists the dis-

tance and frequency of occurrence of well installation in contrast

to the surrogate extracted from the barbecue attendance used in

the MIF. Table XIV shows actual frequency and distance for all

TABLE XIII
PROJECTED AND ACTUAL WELL INSTALLATION FREQUENCY ON THE LOCAL PLANE

Distance (miles)	% Attending Barbecue	% Installing Wells
0-1.0	47.1	54.8
1.1-5.0	20.6	25.3
5.1-10.0	18.2	19.9

393 wells in the Colorado Northern High Plains as compared to the

regional surrogates used in the MIF. For both the local plane and

the regional plane, receiver-teller relationship was more intense

within the first five miles of existing wells than the MIF indicated.

TABLE XIV
PROJECTED AND ACTUAL WELL INSTALLATION FREQUENCY
ON THE REGIONAL PLANE

Distance (miles)	% from MIF	% Installing Wells
0-5.0	58.0	63.2
5.1-10.0	29.0	25.2
10.1-20.0	9.0	11.1
more than 20	.4	.2

recharge program that as yet is undeterminable in terms of success
or failure--however, there has been little continued well installation in the Cope area because of serious drawdown in the shallow
alluvial wells. Another atypical situation is the lack of surface
irrigation development down stream from Bonny Reservoir located
in Southeastern Yuma County. In brief, it is a rather expensive
"white elephant" financed primarily by federal funds. Once completed, it was found that the extensive ranch and farm holdings
downstream were not interested in converting to irrigation. In
what might have been an irrigated oasis almost 10 years ago, there
has been practically no development, and it seems destined to continue as a "well engineered but poorly planned project."

The probable explanation is the increase in multi-well ownership and the tendency to install the second well adjacent to the first.

The multi-well ownership accounts for the most apparent midjudgment in the model, which was the use of pair-wise generation with only one well telling another well in any one year. It seems that for a brief time, an existing well not only generates the idea to an adjacent potential irrigator but also "tells its own owner." Preliminary data suggests a rapid increase in multi-well ownership, which creates both a greater concentration and a rapid increase in number. However, as a method of long term projection, the approximation by the models will probably remain valid because (1) as saturation occurs it becomes more difficult to find an open irrigable space within a township to install a well; and, (2) control and regulations are going to be established within the near future. In fact, members of the Northeastern Colorado Development Committee have favored the 16 well per township saturation limit for Class I and II land (with 500 gpm) as a legal upper limit.

A summarization and future outlook for the Colorado Northern High Plains should be easy after five years of contact and investigation. But, as is often the case, the projection must lie in the transition area between proved fact and biased opinion. It would be unfair to avoid or pass over what appears to be the most important aspect of the future environment--which is change, transition that is taking place and is apparently irreversible. The change is bringing about the disappearance of the family farm, a decrease in farm population, and a tendency toward bigger and more complicated enterprises.

Several people still speculate that pump irrigation will curtail the death of the family farm for several generations. Paradoxically, irrigation is accelerating the process rather than retarding it, and will probably continue to do so as it forces many small operators out of business due to high investment and maintenance costs.

Mechanization has made the small farm obsolete, and any operator in the Colorado Northern High Plains who farms less than 1000 acres (with or without irrigation) is in an economic squeeze. In the present society where low income farm products must be subsidized by the urban tax dollar, adjustments have to be made. Eventually, the agricultural economy of the Colorado Northern High Plains must compete and the low income per unit of effort and per unit of land will not permit the survival of any but well-planned resource use which is managed with intense care on an extensive scale. In order to do this, machines must be used to their utmost advantage. Increasing the scale of operation, reducing the division of income, and maximizing the use of implements is the only way the area can successfully compete in the mechanically oriented agriculture world of tomorrow. As pedantic as it may sound, the farming activities need "Quality Control."

The present agriculturalist has three rather limited choices: (1) Extract as much as possible from the land for the greatest gain so he can educate his children, invest elsewhere, etc., and do all possible in preparing to abandon farm life. The dangers to the region are obvious as this encourages resource mismanagement and destruction. (2) Participate in the stop gap movements (such as irrigation, new seed varieties, fertilization, etc.) in the hope that the living environment may be sustained under present conditions for as long as permissible with government support. (3) Expand on available credit, acquire land and equipment, with the assumption he will be one of the few operators or owners in the coming corporate farm era. None of the three choices is clear cut, and many farmers are trying to combine them all at once.

The future of agriculture in the Colorado Northern High Plains lies in the hands of a few individuals. In the competition to come, there will be few winners and many losers as the transition to corporate agriculture is made. Only the shrewd, well financed, enlightened resource manager will be able to survive under the complexities of corporated, unsubsidized, competitive agriculture. And only the ingenious will do it on a long term basis. However, in terms of future national and world benefits, we need this type of ingenuity to feed the world's expanding urban population.

SELECTED BIBLIOGRAPHY

Books

Brown, Ralph H., *Historical Geography of the United States*, New York: Harcourt, Brace and Company, 1951.

Ciriacy-Wantrup, S. V., *Resource Conservation*, Berkeley, Calif.: University of California, Division of Agricultural Sciences, 1963.

Dunn, Edgar S., *The Location of Agricultural Production*, Gainesville: University of Florida Press, 1954.

Feller, William, *An Introduction to Probability Theory and its Application*, Vol. 1, New York: John Wiley & Sons, 1950.

Fenneman, Nevin M., *Physiography of Western United States*, New York: McGraw-Hill Book Company, 1931.

Firey, Walter, *Man, Mind, and Land*, Glencoe, Illinois: The Free Press, 1960.

Higbee, Edward, *American Agriculture: Geography, Resources, Conservation*, New York: John Wiley and Sons, Inc., 1958.

_____, *Farms and Farmers in an Urban Age*, New York: The Twentieth Century Fund, 1963.

Johnson, Vance, *Heaven's Tableland*, New York: Farrar, Straus, and Company, 1947.

Griffin, John I., *Statistics, Methods and Applications*, New York: Holt, Rinehart and Wintson, 1962.

Hagerstrand, Torsten, *The Propagation of Innovation Waves*, Lund, Sweden: The Royal University of Lund, Studies in Geography, Series B., Human Geography, No. 4, 1952.

_____, *Innovationsforloppet Ur Korologisk Synpunkt*, Lund, Sweden: Gleerupska University, Bokhanded, 1953.

Kraenzel, Carl Frederick, *The Great Plains in Transition*, Norman: The University of Oklahoma Press, 1955.

Lionberger, Herbert F., _Adoption of New Ideas and Practices_, Ames, Iowa: Iowa State University Press, 1960.

Meinzer, O. E., ed. _Hydrology_, Vol. IX of _Physics of the Earth_, New York: McGraw-Hill Book Company, 1942.

Rogers, Everett M., _Diffusion of Innovations_, New York: Free Press of Glencoe, 1962.

Steinel, Alvin T. and D. C. Working, _History of Agriculture in Colorado_, Fort Collins, Colorado: State Agricultural College, 1926.

Thomas, C. F., _Ground Water Conservation_, New York: McGraw-Hill Book Company, 1951.

Todd, D. C., _Ground Water Hydrology_, New York: John Wiley and Sons, Inc., 1959.

Toleman, C. F., _Ground Water_, New York: McGraw-Hill Book Company, 1937.

Weaver, J. E. and F. W. Albertson, _Grasslands of the Great Plains: Their Nature and Use_, Lincoln: L. Johnson Publishing Company, 1956.

Webb, Walter Prescott, _The Great Plains_, Boston: Ginn and Company, 1931.

Articles and Pamphlets

Bailey, Warren R., "Land and Problems in the Wheat Regions," _Land_, the 1958 Yearbook of Agriculture, Washington: United States Government Printing Office, 1958, pp. 150-160.

Beal, George M. and Everett M. Rogers and Joe M. Bohlen, "Validity of the Concept Stages in the Adoption Process," _Rural Sociology_, Vol. 22, No. 3, September 1957.

_____, "How Farmers Accept a New Practice, 2, 4-D: Sources of Information Analyzed by Time," Paper given at Midwest Sociological Society meeting, April 1956.

Bittinger, Morton W., "Colorado Ground Water Problems," Fort Collins, Colorado: Colorado State University Experiment Station, _Bulletin_ 504-S, August 1959.

Blaney, Harry F., "Climate as an Index of Irrigation Needs," _Water_, the 1955 Yearbook of Agriculture, Washington: United States Government Printing Office, 1955, pp. 341-345.

Blaut, J. M., "Mictogeographic Sampling: A Quantitative Approach to Regional Agricultural Geography," Economic Geography, Vol. 35

Bjorkland, L. J. and R. F. Brown, "Geology and Ground Water Resources of the Lower South Platte River Valley Between Hardin, Colorado and Paxton, Nebraska," Geologic Survey Water Supply Paper 1378, Washington: United State Government Printing Office, 1957.

Boettcher, Arnold J. and C. Albert Horr, "Geology and Ground Water Resources in Eastern Cheyenne and Kueva Counties, Colorado," Geological Survey Water-Supply Paper 1779-N, Washington: United States Government Printing Office: 1964.

Cardwell, W. D. E., "Irrigation-well Development in the Kansas River Basin of Eastern Colorado," Geologic Survey Circular 295, Washington, 1953.

_____ and Edward D. Jenkins, "Ground-Water Geology and Pump Irrigation in Frenchman Creek Basin Above Palisade, Nebraska," Geologic Survey Water-Supply Paper: Washington: United States Government Printing Office, 1963.

Chase, George H., Verle M. Burtin, and Thomas J. Major, Colorado Ground Water Basic Data Report No. 10, Kit Carson County, Denver: The United States Geologic Survey in cooperation with the Colorado Water Conservation Board, 1962.

Code, W. E., "Water Table Fluctuations in Eastern Colorado," Fort Collins, Colorado: Colorado State University Experiment Station, Bulletin 504-S, August 1959.

Colby, Charles C., The Kansas Basin, Pilot Study of a Water Shed, University of Kansas Press, 1956.

Dodd, Stuart C., "Duffusion is Predictable: Testing Probability Models for Laws of Interaction," American Sociological Review, Vol. 20, August 1955.

Durand, Loyal, Jr., "American Centralizer Belt," Economic Geography, Vol. 31, 1955, pp. 301-320.

Farmer, Edward J., "Colorado's Ground Water Problems, " Fort Collins, Colorado: Colorado State University Experiment Station, Bulletin 505-S, 1960.

Garrison, William L., "Notes on the Simulation of Urban Growth and Development," Occasional Papers, Canadian Association of Geographers, British Columbia Dominion: No. 1, 1960, pp. 1-11.

_____, "Toward Simulation Models of Urban Growth and Development," in Knut Norborg, ed., Proceedings of the I.G.U. Symposium in Urban Geography, 1960. Lund, Sweden: Royal University of Lund, Studies in Geography, Series B, Human Geography No. 24, 1962, pp. 91-108.

_____ and Duane F. Marble, "The Spatial Structure of Agricultural Activities," Annals, Association of American Geographers, Vol. 47, 1957, pp. 137-144.

Griliches, Zvi, "Hybrid Corn: An Exploration in the Economics of Technological Change," Econometrics, Vol. 25, No. 4, October 1957, pp. 501-522.

Hagerstrand, Torsten, Migration in Sweden, Lund, Sweden: Royal University of Lund, Studies in Geography, Series B, Human Geography No. 13, 1957.

_____, "On Monte Carlo Simulation of Diffusion," Wm. L. Garrison, ed., Quantitative Geography, New York: Atherton Press (forthcoming)

Hewes, Leslie and Arthur C. Schmieding, "Risk in the Central Great Plains: Geographical Patterns of Wheat Failure in Nebraska, 1931-1952," Geographical Review, Vol. 46 July 1956, pp. 375-387.

Hill, D. R. and J. M. Tompkin, "General and Engineering Geology of the Wray Area, Colorado and Nebraska," United States Geologic Survey Bulletin 1001, 1953.

Hudson, G. D., "Methods Employed by Geographers in Regional Surveys," Economic Geography, Vol. 12, 1936, pp. 98-104.

Kollmorgen, Walter M. and George F. Jenks, "Sidewalk Farming in Toole County, Montana, and Traill County, North Dakota," Annals, Association of American Geographers, Vol. 48, December 1958, pp. 375-397.

_____ and George F. Jenks, "Suitcase Farming in Sully County, South Dakota," Annals, Association of American Geographers, Vol. 48, March 1958, pp. 27-40.

Kulldorff, Gunnar, Migration Probabilities, Lund, Sweden: Royal University of Lund, Studies in Geography, Series B., Human Geography, No. 14, 1955.

Johnson, W. D. "The High Plains and Their Utilization," Twenty-first Annual Report of United States Geological Survey, Vol. IV, Washington: United States Government Printing Office, 1901, pp. 601-741.

Johnson, Glenn L. and Cecil B. Haver, "Decision Making Principles in Farm Management," Kentucky Agricultural Experiment Station Bulletin 593, Lexington, January 1953.

"Irrigation in the Midwest," Business Conditions, Federal Reserve Bank of Chicago, December 1956, pp. 13-16.

Lionberger, Herbert F. and C. Milton Coughenor, "Social Structure and Diffusion of Farm Information," Agricultural Experiment Station, College of Agriculture, University of Missouri, Research Bulletin 631, April 1957.

_____, "Neighborhoods as a Factor in the Diffusion of Farm Information in a Northeast Missouri Community," Rural Sociology, Vol. 19, No. 4, December 1954, pp. 377-384.

Loeffler, M. John, "Beet Sugar Production on the Colorado Piedmont," Annals, Association of American Geographers, Vol. 53, September 1963, pp. 364-374.

Marsh, C. Paul, "Farmers' Practice-Adoption Rates in Relation to Adoption Rates of 'Leaders'," Rural Sociology, Vol. 19, No. 2, June 1954, pp. 180-183.

_____, "Group Influences and Agricultural Innovations: Some Tentative Findings and Hypotheses," American Journal of Sociology, Vol. 61, No. 6, May 1956.

McGovern, Harold E., "Geology and Ground-Water Resources of Washington County, Colorado," Geological Survey Water-Supply Paper 1777, Washington: United States Government Printing Office, 1964.

_____, "Records, Logs, and Water-Level Measurements of Selected Wells and Test Holes, and Chemical Analyses of Ground Water in Washington County, Colorado," Colorado Ground Water Basic Data Report No. 6, Denver: The United States Geological Survey in cooperation with the Colorado Water Conservation Board, 1961.

McVoy, Edgar C., "Patterns of Diffusion in the United States," American Sociological Review, Vol. 5, No. 2, April 1940, pp. 219-227.

Morrill, Richard L. and Forest R. Pitts, "Marriage, Migration and the Mean Information Field: a Study in Uniqueness and Generality," (Hectographed).

Nystuen, John D., "A Simulation Model of Interurban Travel," W. L. Garrison, ed., Quantitative Geography.

Pedersen, Harald A., "Cultural Differences in the Acceptance of Recommended Practices," Rural Sociology, Vol. 16, No. 1, March 1951. pp. 37-49.

Pitts, Forest R., "Problems in Computer Simulation of Diffusion," Papers and Proceedings, The Regional Science Association, 1963.

_____, "Chorology Revisited--Computerwise," The Professional Geographer, Vol. 14, 1962.

Robinson, Arthur H., "The Necessity of Weighing Value in Correlation Analysis of Areal Data," Annals, Association of American Geographers, Vol. 46, 1956, pp. 233-236.

_____, J. H. Lindberg and L. Brinkman, "A Correlation and Regression Analysis Applied to Rural Farm Population Densities in the Great Plains," Annals, Association of American Geographers, Vol. 51, 1961, pp. 211-222.

Rogers, Everett M. and George M. Beal, "An Approach to Measure Reference Group Influences in the Adoption of Farm Practices," Paper presented at Rural Sociological Society, August 1957, College Park, Maryland.

_____ and George M. Beal, "The Importance of Personal Influence in the Adoption of Technological Change," Social Forces, Vol. 36, No. 4, May 1958, pp. 329-335.

Rohwer, Carl, "Wells and Pumps for Irrigated Lands," Water, the 1955 Yearbook of Agriculture, Washington: United States Government Printing Office, Department of Agriculture, 1955, pp. 285-294.

Ryan, Bryce and Neal Gross, "The Diffusion of Hybrid Seed Corn in Two Iowa Communities," Rural Sociology, Vol. 8, No. 1, March 1943, pp. 15-24.

_____, "A Study of Technological Diffusion," Rural Sociology, Vol. 13, No. 3, September 1948, pp. 273-285.

Strahler, Arthur, "Statistical Analysis in Geomorphic Research," Journal of Geology, Vol. 62, 1954.

_____ and D. Koons, "Objective and Quantitative Field Methods of Terrain Analysis," Columbia University Department of Geology, Report, 1960.

Thornthwaite, C. Warren, "Climate and Settlement in the Great Plains," Climate and Man, the 1941 Yearbook of Agriculture, United States Department of Agriculture, Washington: U. S. Government Printing Office, 1941, pp. 177-187.

"United States Department of Agriculture Annual Inventory," _Farm Credit Conditions_, The Farm Credit Banks of Wichita, Vol. XXVI, 2 and 3, February-March 1961.

"U. S. Farms, Prices Received, and Prices Paid by Farmers 1945-1963," Research Division, Farm Credit Banks of Wichita, December 1963.

Weaver, John C., et al., "Livestock Units and Combination Regions in the Middle West," Economic Geography, Vol. 32, July, 1956, p. 259.

Weist, William G. Jr., "Geology and Ground Water Resources of Yuma County, Colorado," _Geological Water Supply Paper 1539-J_, Washington: U. S. Government Printing Office, 1964.

_____, "Records and Logs of Selected Wells and Test Holes, and Chemical Analyses of Ground Water, Yuma County, Colorado," _Colorado Ground Water Basic Data Report No. 2_, 1960. United States Geologic Survey in cooperation with the Colorado Water Conservation Board, Denver, Colorado.

"Wheat Surplus Problem, The," _Monthly Review_, Federal Reserve Bank of Kansas City, November 1960, pp. 10-16.

Wilkening, E. A., "Sources of Information for Improved Farm Practices," _Rural Sociology_, Vol. 15, No. 1, March 1950, pp. 19-30.

Zobler, Leonard, "Decision Making in Regional Construction," _Annals_, Association of American Geographers, Vol. 48, 1958, pp. 140-148.

                        Miscellaneous

Bowden, Leonard W., "Pump Irrigation in the Northern Colorado High Plains," Doctoral Thesis, Clark University, 1964.

_____, "Pump Irrigation in Western Yuma County: An Environmental Adjustment," Masters Thesis, University of Colorado, 1961.

Colorado Yearbook, Denver, Colorado, 1943-1962.

Cooperative Consumer, The, Kansas City, Missouri, June 30, 1962.

Farm Credit Conditions, Wichita, Kansas, January 1961-July 1963.

Monthly Review, Federal Reserve Bank of Kansas City.

Sterling (Colorado) Advocate, January 17, 1962.

Wray (Colorado) Gazette, January 1960 - January 1963.

Yuma (Colorado) Pioneer, July 1960 - July 1963.

Addendum

Hewes, Leslie, "A Traverse Across Kit Carson County, Colorado,
     with notes on Land Use on the Margin of the Old Dust
     Bowl, 1939-40 and 1962," Economic Geography, Volume 39,
     No. 4, October, 1963, pp. 332-340.

THE UNIVERSITY OF CHICAGO
DEPARTMENT OF GEOGRAPHY
RESEARCH PAPERS (Planographed, 6 × 9 Inches)

(Available from Department of Geography, Rosenwald Hall, University of Chicago, Chicago 37, Illinois. Price: four dollars each; by series subscription, three dollars each.)

* Out of print.

*49. MAYER, HAROLD M. *The Port of Chicago and the St. Lawrence Seaway*

50. PATTISON, WILLIAM D. *Beginnings of the American Rectangular Land Survey System, 1784–1800*

51. BROWN, ROBERT HAROLD. *Political Areal-Functional Organization: With Special Reference to St. Cloud, Minnesota.* 1957. 130 pp.

52. BEYER, JACQUELYN. *Integration of Grazing and Crop Agriculture: Resources Management Problems in the Uncompahgre Valley Irrigation Project.* 1957. 131 pp.

53. ACKERMAN, EDWARD A. *Geography as a Fundamental Research Discipline* 1958. 40 pp. $1.00.

*54. AL-KHASHAB, WAFIQ HUSSAIN. *The Water Budget of the Tigris and Euphrates Basin*

55. LARIMORE, ANN EVANS. *The Alien Town: Patterns of Settlement in Busoga, Uganda* 1958. 210 pp.

56. MURPHY, FRANCIS C. *Regulating Flood-Plain Development* 1958. 216 pp.

*57. WHITE, GILBERT F., *et al.* *Changes in Urban Occupance of Flood Plains in the United States*

58. COLBY, MARY MC RAE. *The Geographic Structure of Southeastern North Carolina* 1958. 242 pp.

*59. MEGEE, MARY CATHERINE. *Monterrey, Mexico: Internal Patterns and External Relations*

60. WEBER, DICKINSON. *A Comparison of Two Oil City Business Centers (Odessa-Midland, Texas)* 1958. 256 pp.

61. PLATT, ROBERT S. *Field Study in American Geography* 1959. 408 pp.

62. GINSBURG, NORTON, editor. *Essays on Geography and Economic Development* 1960. 196 pp.

63. HARRIS, CHAUNCY D., and FELLMANN, JEROME D. *International List of Geographical Serials* 1960. 247 pp.

64. TAAFFE, ROBERT N. *Rail Transportation and the Economic Development of Soviet Central Asia* 1960. 186 pp.

65. SHEAFFER, JOHN R. *Flood Proofing: An Element in a Flood Damage Reduction Program* 1960. 190 pp.

66. RODGERS, ALLAN L. *The Industrial Geography of the Port of Genova* 1960. 150 pp.

67. KENYON, JAMES B. *Industrial Localization and Metropolitan Growth: The Paterson-Passaic District.* 1960. 250 pp.

68. GINSBURG, NORTON. *An Atlas of Economic Development* 1961. 119 pp. 14 × 8½″. Paper $5.00; Cloth $7.50. University of Chicago Press.

69. CHURCH, MARTHA. *Spatial Organization of Electric Power Territories in Massachusetts* 1960. 200 pp.

70. WHITE, GILBERT F., *et al.* *Papers on Flood Problems* 1961. 234 pp.

71. GILBERT, E. W. *The University Town in England and West Germany* 1961. 79 pp. 4 plates. 30 maps and diagrams.

72. BOXER, BARUCH. *Ocean Shipping in the Evolution of Hong Kong* 1961. 108 pp.

73. ROBINSON, IRA M. *New Industrial Towns on Canada's Resource Frontier* 1962. (Research Paper No. 4, Program of Education and Research in Planning, The University of Chicago.) 192 pp

74. TROTTER, JOHN E. *State Park System in Illinois* 1962. 152 pp.

75. BURTON, IAN. *Types of Agricultural Occupance of Flood Plains in the United States* 1962. 167 pp.

76. PRED, ALLAN. *The External Relations of Cities During 'Industrial Revolution'* 1962. 124 pp.

77. BARROWS, HARLAN H. *Lectures on the Historical Geography of the United States as Given in 1933* Edited by WILLIAM A. KOELSCH. 1962. 248 pp.

78. KATES, ROBERT WILLIAM. *Hazard and Choice Perception in Flood Plain Management* 1962. 157 pp.

79. HUDSON, JAMES. *Irrigation Water Use in the Utah Valley, Utah* 1962. 249 pp.

80. ZELINSKY, WILBUR. *A Bibliographic Guide to Population Geography* 1962. 257 pp.

*81. DRAINE, EDWIN H. *Import Traffic of Chicago and Its Hinterland*

82. KOLARS, JOHN F. *Tradition, Season, and Change in a Turkish Village* NAS-NRC Foreign Field Research Program Report No. 15. 1963. 205 pp.

83. WIKKRAMATILEKE, RUDOLPH. *Southeast Ceylon: Trends and Problems in Agricultural Settlement* 1963. 163 pp.

84. KANSKY, K. J. *Structure of Transportation Networks: Relationships between Network Geometry and Regional Characteristics* 1963. 155 pp.

85. BERRY, BRIAN J. L. *Commercial Structure and Commercial Blight* 1963. 254 pp.

86. BERRY, BRIAN J. L., and TENNANT, ROBERT J. *Chicago Commercial Reference Handbook* 1963.

87. BERRY, BRIAN J. L., and HANKINS, THOMAS D. *A Bibliographic Guide to the Economic Regions of the United States* 1963. 128 pp.

88. MARCUS, MELVIN G. *Climate-Glacier Studies in the Juneau Ice Field Region, Alaska* 1964. 128 pp.

89. SMOLE, WILLIAM J. *Owner-Cultivatorship in Middle Chile* 1964. 176 pp.

90. HELVIG, MAGNE. *Chicago's External Truck Movements: Spatial Interaction between the Chicago Area and Its Hinterland* 1964. 132 pp.

91. HILL, A. DAVID. *The Changing Landscape of a Mexican Municipio, Villa Las Rosas, Chiapas* NAS-NRC Foreign Field Research Program Report No. 26. 1964. 121 pp.

92. SIMMONS, JAMES W. *The Changing Pattern of Retail Location* 1964. 212 pp.

93. WHITE, GILBERT F. *Choice of Adjustment to Floods* 1964. 164 pp.

94. MC MANIS, DOUGLAS R. *The Initial Evaluation and Utilization of the Illinois Prairies, 1815–1840* 1964. 109 pp.

95. PERLE, EUGENE D. *The Demand for Transportation: Regional and Commodity Studies in the United States* 1964. 130 pp.

96. HARRIS, CHAUNCY D. *Annotated World List of Selected Current Geographical Serials in English.* 1964. 32 pp. $1.00

97. BOWDEN, LEONARD W. *Diffusion of the Decision To Irrigate: Simulation of the Spread of a New Resource Management Practice in the Colorado Northern High Plains* 1965. 146 pp.

*Out of print.